100% Language

Activities for Language Comprehension

Patti Halfman

Skill Area:	Language & Listening
Ages:	5 thru 9
Grades:	K thru 4

LinguiSystems, Inc.
3100 4th Avenue
East Moline, IL 61244-9700
1-800-PRO IDEA
1-800-776-4332

FAX: 1-800-577-4555
E-mail: service@linguisystems.com
Web: www.linguisystems.com
TDD: 1-800-933-8331
(for those with hearing impairments)

Printed in the U.S.A.

ISBN 0-7606-0405-3

About the Author

Patti Halfman, M.A., CCC-SLP, is a speech-language pathologist who spends her work day talking with LinguiSystems customers. Before joining the staff of LinguiSystems, Patti worked in various school settings helping children in preschool through high school.

This is Patti's second publication with LinguiSystems. She is also co-author of *Scissors, Glue, and Vocabulary, Too!*

Dedication

To the special people in my life—
for your inspiration, support, laughter,
and friendship, thank you

Illustrations by Margaret Warner
Cover Design by Chris Claus
Edited by Kelly Malone
Page Layout by Lisa Parker

Table of Contents

Introduction

Do your students struggle with language tasks? Do they experience difficulty mastering, or even acquiring, basic language skills? If so, they are undoubtedly frustrated with our complex language. Unfortunately, they may begin to experience problems in other areas as well such as self-expression, decision-making, social development, reading, and math. However, if you can head trouble off at the pass, the road to success will be much smoother for your students. *100% Language Comprehension—Primary* is full of ready-to-use activities designed to help you do just that. Once your students learn these skills and begin to understand and use language more effectively, they will become more successful in other areas as well.

100% Language Comprehension–Primary is divided into six language areas that progress in difficulty throughout each unit:

- Reasoning
- Sequencing
- Cause & Effect
- Problem Solving
- Opinions
- Inferencing

Each unit includes the following components:

- Overview
- Progress Chart
- 24 activity pages
- Family Letter

Overview

The overview offers a brief description of the unit, additional suggestions for introducing the unit and using the activity pages, and expansion activities to help you provide opportunities for your students to generalize what they've learned.

Progress Chart

The progress chart is a tool you can use to keep track of the activities a student has completed and record any comments you might have on his performance.

Activity Pages

Activities 1-20 progress in difficulty throughout each unit. You'll notice that some of these pages contain pictures. Occasionally the pictures will give the student a clue to the answer; however, they generally do not provide answers to the questions. Rather, they are included on the page for students who benefit from visual cues to trigger their thought processes. The pictures may also be beneficial when working with ESL students or students who have a more limited vocabulary. Pages requiring the same language skill but without pictures are always provided.

Activities 21-24 in each unit are picture scenes. I've included these scenes in order to provide students with a more theme-based approach in which to apply the learned skills. The questions on these pages incorporate various levels of language comprehension that students have practiced earlier in the unit. As a result, keep in mind that younger students may not be able to respond to some of the more complex questions. Additionally, for older students, you may choose to reword some of the less-challenging questions to increase their difficulty. You may also want to ask additional questions not provided on these pages.

The activities are designed for one-on-one or classroom use with students ages five through nine, grades K through four. Many of the activity pages can be presented orally, and students will be able to give their answers verbally or by using gestures (pointing). For activities requiring written work, students will need a pencil or a crayon and occasionally a pair of scissors. Additional materials are needed for one page in the Sequencing unit. Look at the materials list at the top of the page before presenting this activity.

Family Letter

A family letter has been provided for each unit telling parents and caregivers what the child has been learning. There are also some activity ideas for family members to use to help the student continue practicing a particular skill at home.

As you work through the units in *100% Language Comprehension–Primary*, you may notice that there are some similarities across language areas. This is because the targeted language skills are not pure in themselves, but rather, they build one upon the other. I've attempted to separate the tasks enough so that students can focus on one area of language at a time, thereby strengthening it to improve their overall language.

I hope you and your students enjoy this simple approach to improving language comprehension.

Patti

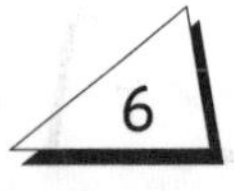

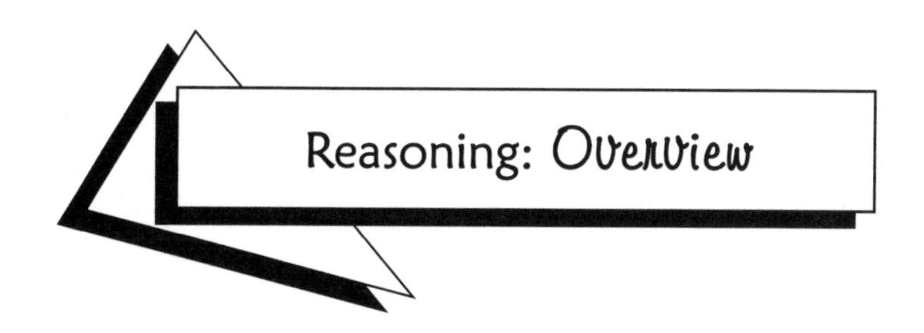

Reasoning is a skill that's necessary for the development of higher-level language skills. As we get older, our language requirements become more and more complex. When students are unable to use language to reason, they often experience difficulty with self-expression, answering questions, comprehending what they hear or read, and solving problems. The activities in this unit are designed to give your students an opportunity to practice basic reasoning skills through everyday situations.

Using the Activity Pages

- Review the vocabulary on each page. Teach any words that may be new to your students.

- Use the format of the questions on a particular page to expand the activity. Ask your students additional questions or have them think of questions to ask each other.

- Analogies are introduced at the end of the unit. If your students are doing well with these basic analogies, you may want to increase the difficulty of the task. Here are a couple of ideas:

    Require students to give two pieces of information. For example, instead of saying "You sit on a chair. You sleep in a ___," you would say "You sit on a ___. You sleep in a ___."

    Present the analogies verbally, this time switching the piece of information you want the child to give. For example, instead of saying "You sit on a chair. You sleep in a ___," change it to "You sit on a chair. You ___ in a bed." By moving the required response within the sentence, the language task is more difficult.

- You may send the activity pages home for additional practice.

Expansion Activities

- During daily activities, talk about what you are doing and why. Ask your students to name materials that you'll need for the activities and tell why they're necessary.

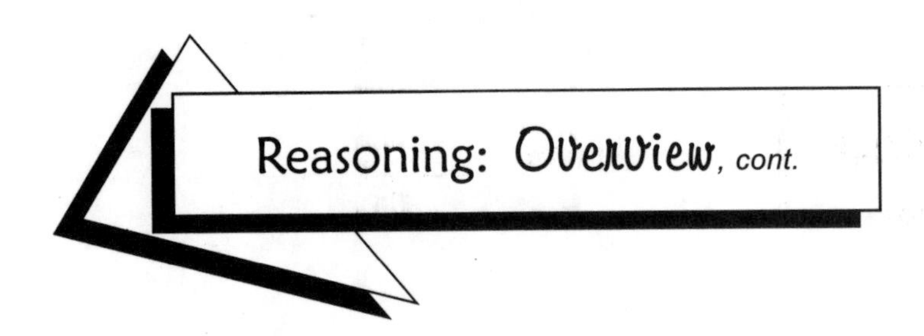

- Have a "Question Word of the Day." Ask each student to take a turn asking a question that begins with the target word. For example, if the word is *Do*, each student will ask a *Do* question like *Do dogs bark?* or *Do pigs fly?* and the other students must answer the questions. Change the question word each day so students get practice with a variety of question words. For older students, focus on higher-level questions.

  You might also incorporate this into a writing activity by asking students to write their questions on paper and then exchange them with one another. Students may respond to the questions verbally or on paper.

- Write the names of categories on index cards. Ask your students to name as many things as they can think of that belong in the categories. Then talk about what each item is for and why it is important. Make the task harder by providing a list of items that belong in a category and including some items that don't belong. Have your students tell which items do and don't belong and why.

Reasoning: Progress Chart

Name________________________

	Days / Trials			Comments
Activity 1				
Activity 2				
Activity 3				
Activity 4				
Activity 5				
Activity 6				
Activity 7				
Activity 8				
Activity 9				
Activity 10				
Activity 11				
Activity 12				
Activity 13				
Activity 14				
Activity 15				
Activity 16				
Activity 17				
Activity 18				
Activity 19				
Activity 20				
Activity 21				
Activity 22				
Activity 23				
Activity 24				

Reasoning: Activity 1

Name_______________________

Listen and then follow my directions.

1. Point to the picture that shows what you use to keep you warm.

2. Point to the picture that shows what you use to rake the yard.

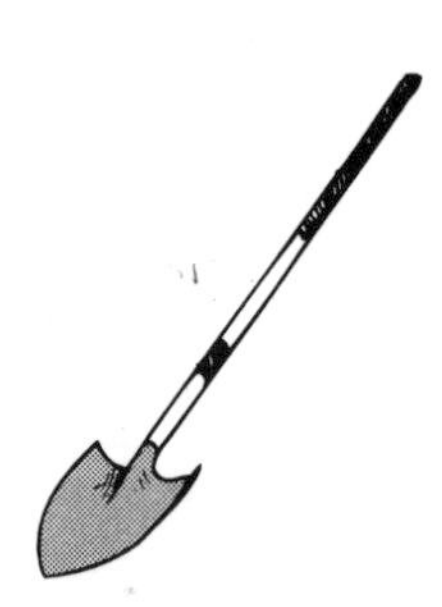

3. Point to the picture that shows when you use an umbrella.

Name____________________

Listen and then follow my directions.

1. Circle the picture that shows why Tom's mom wants to buy a new toaster.

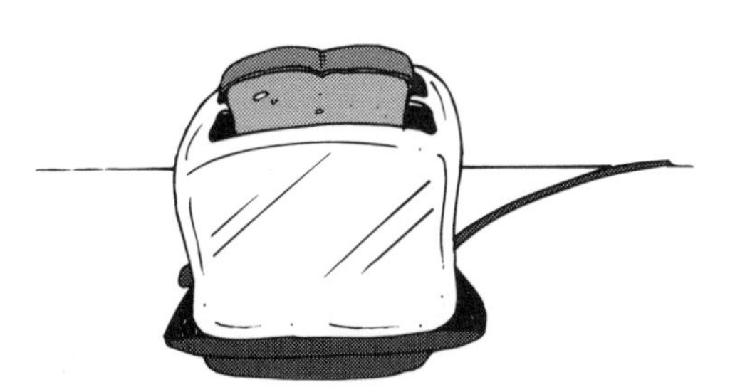

2. Circle the picture that shows something we eat.

3. Circle the picture that shows why Mr. Singer wants to put a fence around his tomato plants.

Reasoning: Activity 3

Name________________________

Listen and then follow my directions.

1. Circle the picture that shows what we use to dry dishes.

2. Circle the picture that shows what we use to listen to music.

3. Circle the picture that shows what we use to build something.

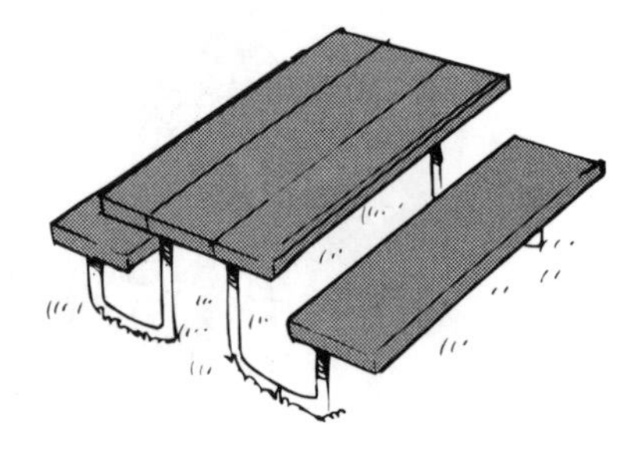

Reasoning: *Activity 4*

Name______________________

Listen and then follow my directions.

1. Mark an **X** on the pictures that show why we need rain.

2. Mark an **X** on the pictures of what we use to draw a picture.

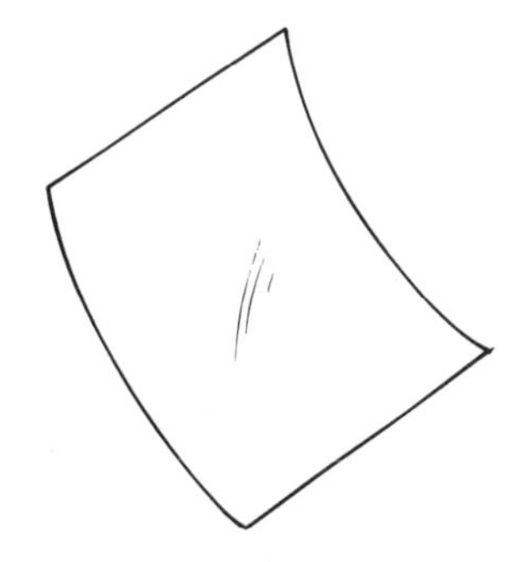

3. Mark an **X** on the pictures of what we use to play baseball.

Name______________________

Look at the first picture in each row. Tell what is happening. Then look at the other pictures in the row. Circle the one that shows why it happened.

1.

2.

3.

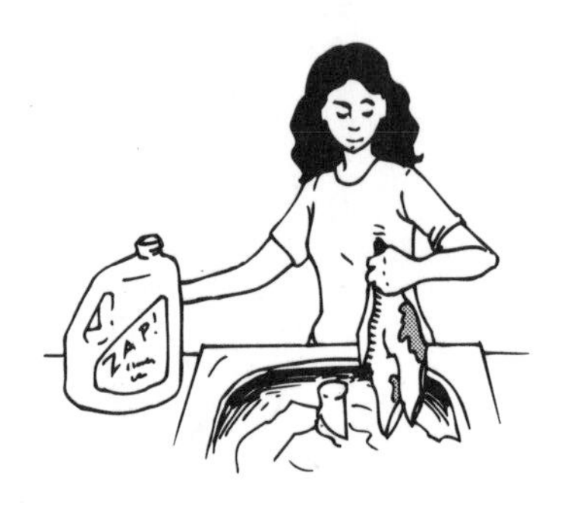

Reasoning: Activity 6

Name________________________

Look at the first picture in each row. Tell what is happening. Then look at the other pictures in the row. Circle the one that shows why it happened.

1.

2.

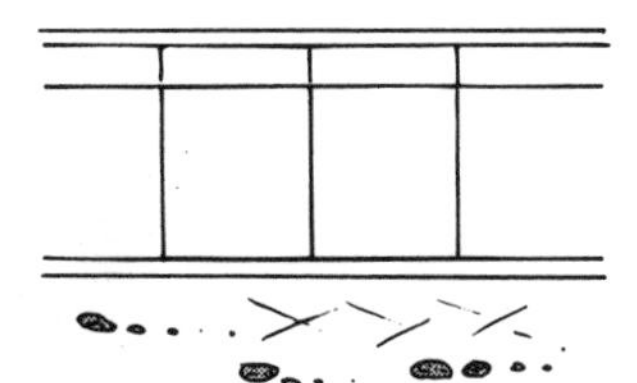

3.

Reasoning: Activity 7

Name________________________

Look at the first picture in each row. Tell what is happening. Then look at the other pictures in the row. Mark an **X** on the one that *doesn't* show why it happened.

1.

2.

3.

Reasoning: *Activity 8*

Name________________________

Listen and then follow my directions.

1. Look at the picture of the man dialing the phone. He's calling the police. Now look at the other pictures in the row. Mark an **X** on each picture that shows why he would call the police.

2. Look at the picture of the girl sitting on the step. She's very tired. Now look at the other pictures in the row. Mark an **X** on each picture that shows why she would be tired.

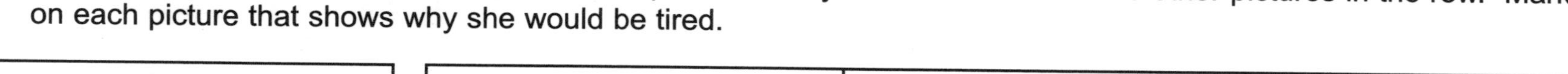

Name____________________

Listen and then follow my directions.

1. Jason and his uncle are going to build a tree house. Mark an **X** on the picture of something Jason and his uncle *don't* need.

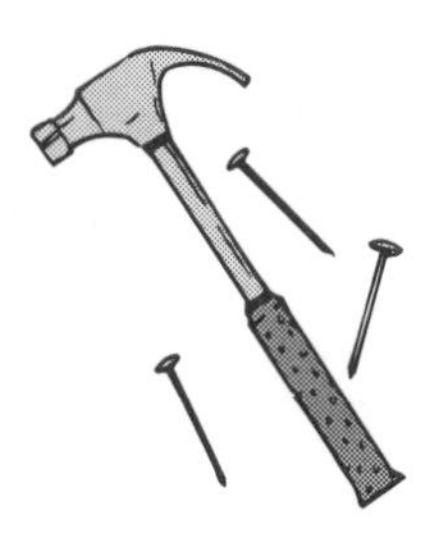

2. Mrs. Harris is going to wash her car. Mark an **X** on the picture of something she *doesn't* need.

3. Pam went to a friend's house to spend the night. Mark an **X** on the picture of something she *doesn't* need to take with her.

Reasoning: Activity 10

Name____________________

Listen to each question I ask. Then circle the correct answer.

1. Can you open a door without using a key? **Yes** **No**
2. Can you ride a bike with no tires? **Yes** **No**
3. Can you eat without using a fork? **Yes** **No**
4. Can you run without wearing shoes? **Yes** **No**
5. Can you wash a car without using water? **Yes** **No**
6. Can you go sledding without any snow? **Yes** **No**
7. Can you cook without using a stove? **Yes** **No**
8. Can you make applesauce without apples? **Yes** **No**
9. Can you play music without a radio? **Yes** **No**
10. Can you play baseball without a bat? **Yes** **No**
11. Can you cut food without using a knife? **Yes** **No**
12. Can you write without using a pencil? **Yes** **No**
13. Can you get a drink without using a glass? **Yes** **No**
14. Can you fill a balloon with water? **Yes** **No**

Name________________________

Listen to each question I ask. Then circle the correct answer.

1.	Do ducks quack?	**Yes**	**No**
2.	Do birds build nests?	**Yes**	**No**
3.	Do pigs have wings?	**Yes**	**No**
4.	Do turtles swim?	**Yes**	**No**
5.	Do fish run?	**Yes**	**No**
6.	Do monkeys fly?	**Yes**	**No**
7.	Do horses eat hay?	**Yes**	**No**
8.	Do rabbits hop?	**Yes**	**No**
9.	Do dogs climb trees?	**Yes**	**No**
10.	Do caterpillars turn into butterflies?	**Yes**	**No**
11.	Do cows eat grass?	**Yes**	**No**
12.	Do snakes have fur?	**Yes**	**No**
13.	Do chickens lay eggs?	**Yes**	**No**
14.	Do turkeys have feathers?	**Yes**	**No**

Reasoning: Activity 12

Name________________________

Listen to each question I ask. Then circle the correct answer.

1. Does a flower bloom? **Yes** **No**
2. Does an egg break if you drop it? **Yes** **No**
3. Does a book roll? **Yes** **No**
4. Does a rubber band stretch? **Yes** **No**
5. Does a fish have to live in water? **Yes** **No**
6. Does a fire burn? **Yes** **No**
7. Does a cat bark? **Yes** **No**
8. Does a baby cry? **Yes** **No**
9. Does a vase hold flowers? **Yes** **No**
10. Does a bus carry people? **Yes** **No**
11. Does a pumpkin bounce? **Yes** **No**
12. Does an airplane go slower than a car? **Yes** **No**
13. Does a boat move on the water? **Yes** **No**
14. Does a stove keep food cold? **Yes** **No**

Reasoning: Activity 13

Name______________________

Listen to each question I ask. Then circle the correct answer.

1.	Do some or all people like music?	**Some**	**All**
2.	Do some or all people drink water?	**Some**	**All**
3.	Do some or all people drive cars?	**Some**	**All**
4.	Do some or all people wear clothes?	**Some**	**All**
5.	Do some or all people use wheelchairs?	**Some**	**All**
6.	Do some or all people live in apartments?	**Some**	**All**
7.	Do some or all people sleep?	**Some**	**All**
8.	Do some or all people like bananas?	**Some**	**All**
9.	Do some or all restaurants serve food?	**Some**	**All**
10.	Do some or all girls play sports?	**Some**	**All**
11.	Do some or all clocks have numbers on them?	**Some**	**All**
12.	Do some or all children walk to school?	**Some**	**All**
13.	Do some or all cars need tires?	**Some**	**All**
14.	Do some or all libraries have books?	**Some**	**All**

Reasoning: Activity 14

Name________________________

Listen to each question I ask. Then circle the correct answer.

1. Is a cat bigger than an elephant? **Yes** **No**
2. Is a mouse smaller than a ladybug? **Yes** **No**
3. Is a man taller than a baby? **Yes** **No**
4. Is fire hotter than smoke? **Yes** **No**
5. Is water colder than ice? **Yes** **No**
6. Is a tree taller than a flower? **Yes** **No**
7. Is cotton softer than a block? **Yes** **No**
8. Is candy sweeter than a lemon? **Yes** **No**
9. Is a rabbit faster than a turtle? **Yes** **No**
10. Is a candle brighter than the sun? **Yes** **No**
11. Is a train slower than a bicycle? **Yes** **No**
12. Is a knife sharper than a spoon? **Yes** **No**
13. Is a snake shorter than a worm? **Yes** **No**
14. Is a bicycle heavier than a motorcycle? **Yes** **No**

Reasoning: Activity 15

Name______________________

Listen and answer my questions. Look at the pictures to help you with your answers.

1. Why do we put ice in water? 

2. Why do people use silverware? 

3. Why do people write letters? 

4. Why do people get their hair cut? 

5. Why do people have jobs? 

6. Why do people laugh at jokes? 

7. Why do we exercise? 

8. Why do we put gas in cars? 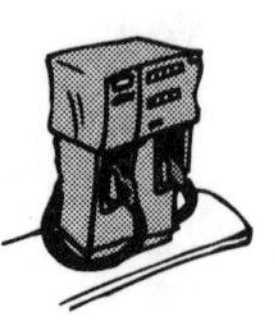

Name____________________

Listen and answer my questions.

1. Why do we ride buses?
2. Why do we use umbrellas?
3. Why do we wear mittens?
4. Why do we drink milk?
5. Why do we wear shoes?
6. Why do we take baths?
7. Why do we brush our teeth?
8. Why do we go to parks?
9. Why do we use soap?
10. Why do people use blankets?
11. Why do people have pets?
12. Why do people eat vegetables?
13. Why do people read books?
14. Why do people lock their doors?
15. Why do people need erasers?

Reasoning: Activity 17

Name________________________

Listen and answer my questions. Look at the pictures to help you with your answers.

1. Why shouldn't we write on walls? 

2. Why shouldn't we hit people? 

3. Why shouldn't we run on the ice? 

4. Why shouldn't we play with matches? 

5. Why shouldn't we pet a dog we don't know? 

6. Why shouldn't we talk to strangers? 

7. Why shouldn't we tear pages from a book? 

8. Why shouldn't we touch a hot stove? 

9. Why shouldn't we go near a swimming pool alone? 

10. Why shouldn't we climb on counters? 

Reasoning: Activity 18

Name____________________________

Look at each picture. I'm going to tell you two reasons for doing each thing. Tell me which reason is better.

1. You should cross the street at the crosswalk because _______.
   a. it's safer
   b. it's the only place to cross the street

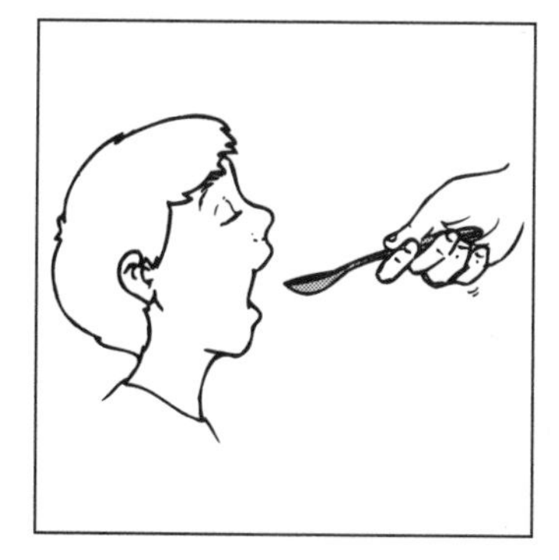

2. It's important to take medicine because _______.
   a. it tastes good
   b. it helps you get well

3. You shouldn't ride your bike in the street because _______.
   a. you could get a flat tire
   b. a car might hit you

Reasoning: Activity 19

Name________________________

Listen and finish my sentence. Look at the pictures to help you with your answer. I'll do the first one for you.

1. You sit on a chair. You sleep in a __*bed*__.

2. A cat has kittens. A dog has _______.

3. You talk to a friend on the phone. You watch a movie on the _______.

4. Water is something you drink. Bread is something you _______.

5. A horse lives on a farm. A zebra lives in a ______.

6. A bird flies. A fish _______.

7. You wear shoes on your feet. You wear gloves on your _______.

8. You color with a crayon. You write with a ______.

Name______________________

Listen and finish my sentence. I'll do the first one for you.

1. A stove keeps food hot. A refrigerator keeps food __*cold*__.
2. A floor is hard. A pillow is _______.
3. You laugh when you are happy. You cry when you are _______.
4. In winter it is cold. In summer it is _______.
5. A rabbit is fast. A turtle is _______.
6. During the day it is light. During the night it is _______.
7. The sky is up. The ground is _______.
8. A block is square. A ball is _______.
9. A camel is big. A hamster is _______.
10. Birds live in trees. Fish live in _______.
11. A dog barks. A cat _______.
12. You wash dishes in a dishwasher. You wash clothes in a _______.
13. You throw a baseball. You kick a _______.
14. A carrot is orange. Lettuce is _______.
15. You eat soup from a bowl. You drink water from a _______.

Name____________________

Look at the picture and answer my questions.

1. Why did the children want to go to the park?
2. Why do you think the children aren't supposed to play on the swing?
3. Why do you think the baby-sitter said it was time to go?
4. Do you think all children like to play at the park? Why?
5. Do you like to play at the park? Why?

Reasoning: Activity 22

Name___________________________

Look at the picture and answer my questions.

1. Is it safe to pet the bears? Why?
2. Do some or all animals live in a zoo?
3. Point to what someone would use to wash the elephant.
4. Why does the zookeeper think the lion is sick?
5. Who do you think the zookeeper will call to help the lion?
6. Why is it important to lock the doors to the animals' pens or cages?

Reasoning: Activity 23

Name________________________

Look at the picture and answer my questions.

1. Mark an **X** on two things the teacher writes on.
2. What could the children use to build a tower?
3. Seven children are in this class. Can some or all of the children sit at the table together?
4. What could the teacher use to play a game called *Number Find*?
5. There's paper on the easel. What else do the children need to draw a picture?
6. What would you like to do if you were in this classroom?

Reasoning: Activity 24

Name___________________________

Look at the picture and answer my questions.

1. Do most people go to the grocery store to buy food?
2. Which one is colder, the ice cream or the milk?
3. Why will the store clerk get a broom and dustpan?
4. What will the people put their groceries in while they're shopping?
5. What will the people put their groceries in to take them home?
6. Finish this sentence. We buy food at a grocery store. We buy gas at a _______.

Dear Family,

I've been learning about reasoning skills. I've learned to talk about why we use things and to answer different questions by thinking about what's been said. You can help me practice by playing one of these games with me.

- We can play a thinking game. First we'll go to a room in our home. Then you name an item, and I'll tell you why we use it. For example, if we were in the kitchen, you might name the stove, and I would tell you that we use it to cook food.

- You might also ask me what item we use to do a particular activity. For example, if we were in the kitchen, you might ask me what we would use to make toast, and I would say "the toaster." We can play these kinds of games in every room of our home!

- Here's another game we can play. First, we'll write the beginning of a question on a sheet of paper, like "Can you eat ___?" Then we'll take turns finishing the question with things like *a nail, a mushroom, a dinosaur, an apple*, or *a squash*. (The questions can be silly if we want them to be!) After one person finishes the question, the other person answers it. Later, we can change the beginning of the question and play the game again.

Thanks for helping me learn!

Love,

____

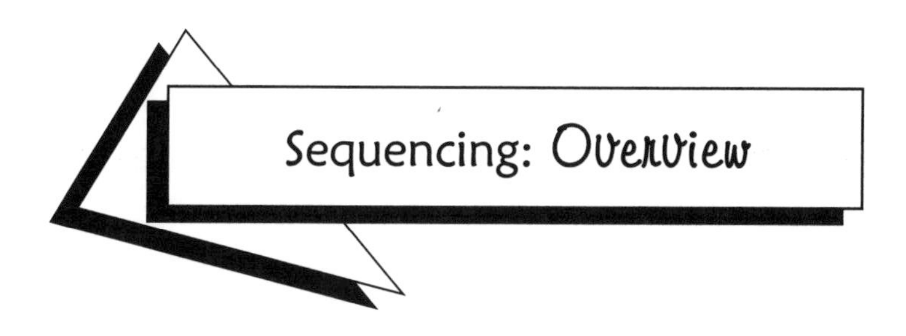

Sequencing is an important language skill for students to acquire at an early age. The ability to sequence impacts a student's success in areas such as following directions, reading and language comprehension, and self-expression.

The activities in this unit include common sequencing vocabulary, patterning, following directions, and sequencing stories and events. As a new type of activity is introduced, there will be reminders to the student to use sequence words when answering questions. These reminders will be faded out, but you may choose to continue to include them as necessary.

Using the Activity Pages

- Review the vocabulary on each page. Teach any words that are new to your students. If it is not already part of the activity, you may choose to have your students cut out sequence pictures and put them in order. Then have them tell a story about the pictures.
- Only two pages are provided for sequencing by pattern, size, weight, etc. Prior to doing each of these pages, you may want to bring in actual objects for your students to sequence. You may also choose to create additional activity sheets for each task.
- Use the activity pages to send home for additional practice.

Expansion Activities

- Have your students create patterns with beads, different coins, buttons, etc.
- Ask your students to find patterns in things like clothing or the floor tiles and talk about them.
- Take pictures of your students doing various activities. Later, have them put the pictures in the order they happened. Then have them tell about the activities.
- Videotape your students doing various activities. Later, watch the film without sound, and have your students create their own stories. Then have them share their stories.

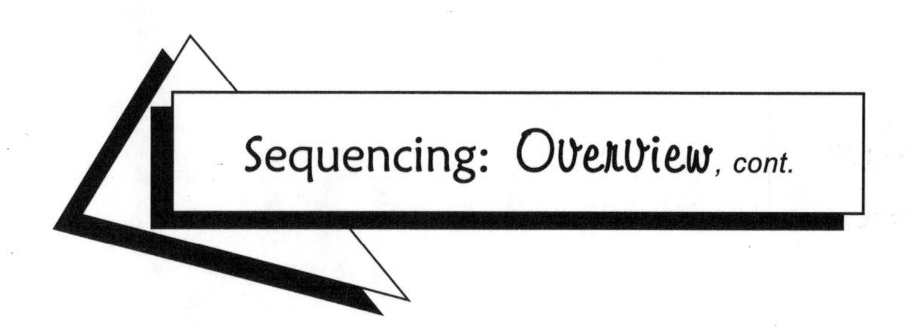

- Read a story and talk about beginning, middle, and end. Ask your students questions about the sequence events in the story. While reading to your students, have them draw pictures of what is happening. Later, have them take turns retelling the story.

- Use a calendar each day as you talk about the days of the week and the months of the year.

- Talk about the daily classroom schedule of events at the beginning or end of the day. Ask your students a variety of questions requiring them to sequence what will or has happened.

- Do activities involving sequencing of letters and numbers.

- Play barrier games to practice following directions.

- For students who continue to have difficulty sequencing and following directions, break information into smaller parts.

- Have students repeat directions before beginning an activity.

- Introduce new sequence vocabulary like *yesterday*, *tomorrow*, *early*, and *late* as your students are ready.

Name________________________

	Days / Trials			Comments
Activity 1				
Activity 2				
Activity 3				
Activity 4				
Activity 5				
Activity 6				
Activity 7				
Activity 8				
Activity 9				
Activity 10				
Activity 11				
Activity 12				
Activity 13				
Activity 14				
Activity 15				
Activity 16				
Activity 17				
Activity 18				
Activity 19				
Activity 20				
Activity 21				
Activity 22				
Activity 23				
Activity 24				

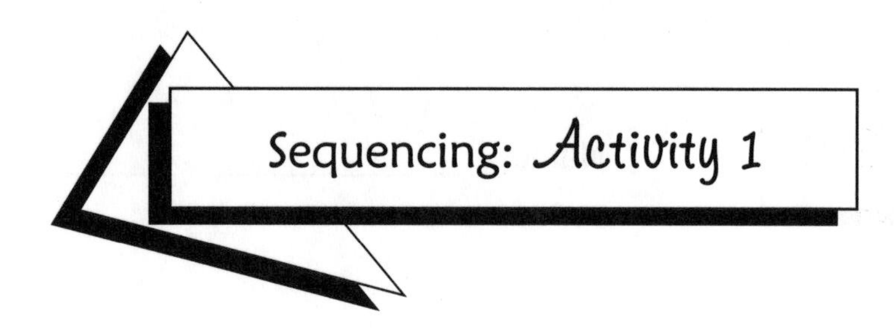

Sequencing: Activity 1

Name______________________

Listen and then follow my directions.

1. Nate poured cereal in a bowl. Circle the picture that shows what Nate did next.

2. Bailey's grandma gave her a present. Circle the picture that shows what Bailey did next.

3. Mrs. Carney thought the grass was too long. Circle the picture that shows what Mrs. Carney did next.

Sequencing: *Activity 2*

Name________________________

Listen and then follow my directions.

1. Look at the pictures of the dog. Point to the picture that shows how the dog looked before she got her hair cut.

2. Look at the pictures of the shirt. Point to the picture that shows how the shirt looked before Mom washed it.

3. Look at the pictures of the clown. Point to the picture of the clown before he put his make-up on.

4. Look at the pictures of the sheets of paper. Point to the picture that shows how the paper looked before Karen drew her picture.

Sequencing: Activity 3

Name________________________

Listen and then follow my directions.

1. Look at the pictures of laundry. Mark an **X** on the picture that shows how the laundry looked after Dad folded it.

2. Look at the pictures of the snowman. Mark an **X** on the picture that shows how the snowman looked after the boy built it.

3. Look at the pictures of the boy. Mark an **X** on the picture that shows the boy after he was ready for school.

4. Look at the pictures of Kelsey's room. Mark an **X** on the picture that shows what her room looked like after she cleaned it.

Sequencing: *Activity* 4

Name____________________

Listen and then follow my directions.

1. Look at the children at the drinking fountain. Point to the first child in line.

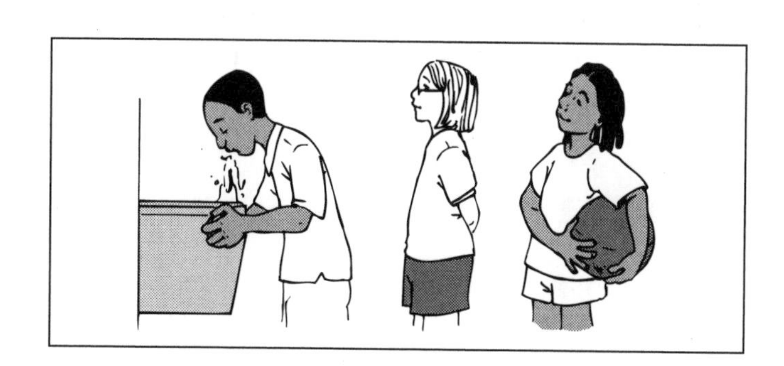

2. Look at the cars stopped at the stoplight. Point to the car that is first in line.

3. Look at the pictures of the cake. Kayla is going to decorate the cake. Point to the picture that shows the first thing Kayla will do.

4. Look at the pictures of Jeremy. He wants a drink of water. Point to the picture that shows the first thing Jeremy will do.

Sequencing: Activity 5

Name____________________

Listen and then follow my directions.

1. Look at the chairs. Circle the last chair in the row.

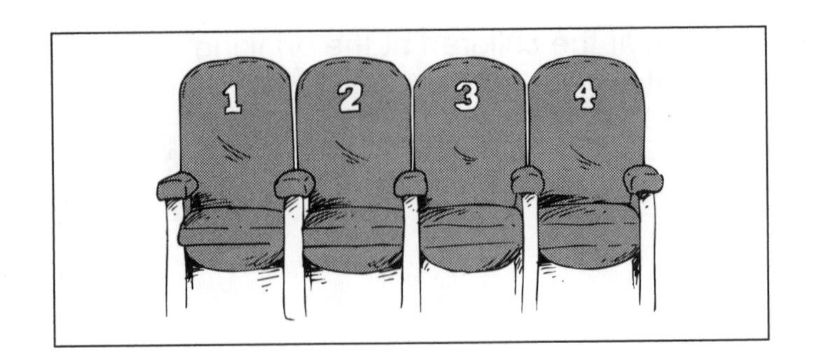

2. Look at the people outside the building. Circle the person who was the last one to leave.

3. Look at the pictures of Mrs. Cunnick. She's leaving her apartment. Circle the picture that shows the last thing she will do.

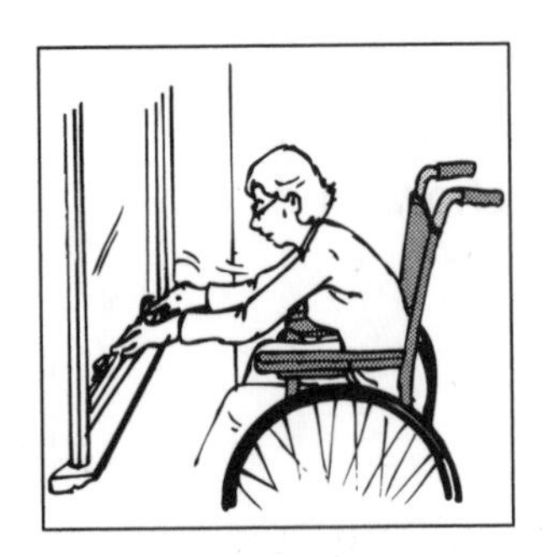

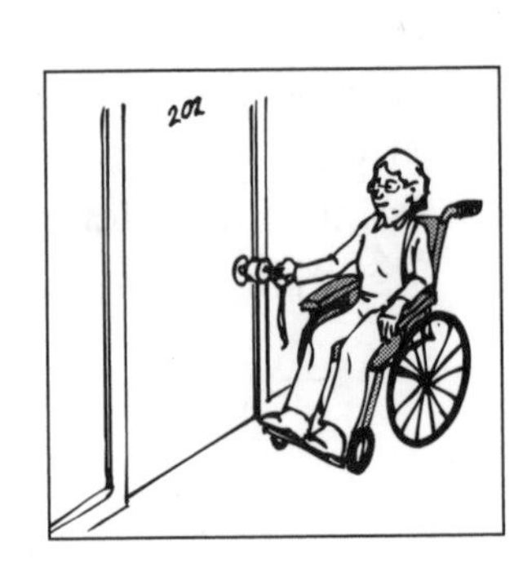

4. Look at the pictures of Tyler. Circle the picture that shows the last thing he will do before going to sleep.

Sequencing: Activity 6

Name____________________

Listen and then follow my directions.

1. Look at the butterflies. Draw a line under the second butterfly.

2. Look at the flowers. Mark an **X** on the second flower.

3. Look at the ladybugs. Circle the second ladybug.

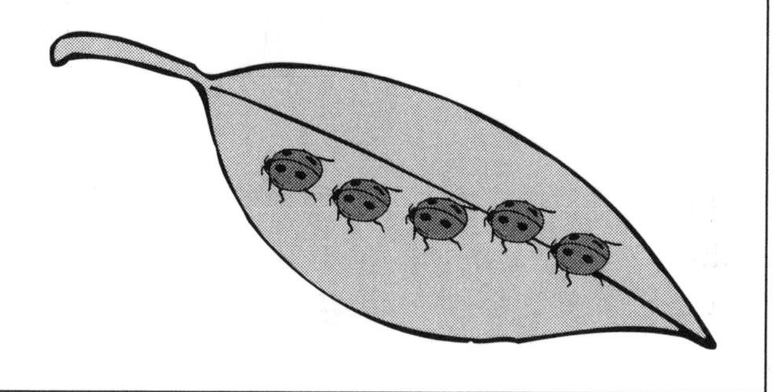

Sequencing: Activity 7

Name____________________

Listen and then follow my directions.

1. Look at the trees. Draw a box around the third tree.

2. Look at the cupcakes. Circle the third cupcake.

3. Look at the ducks. Color the third duck.

Sequencing: *Activity 8*

Name_______________________

Look at the rows of numbers, letters, and pictures. Each row has a pattern. Write what would come next in each pattern.

1.

1 2   1 2 3   1 2   1 2 3

2.

A   B B   A   B B   A   B B

3.

   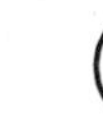   

4.

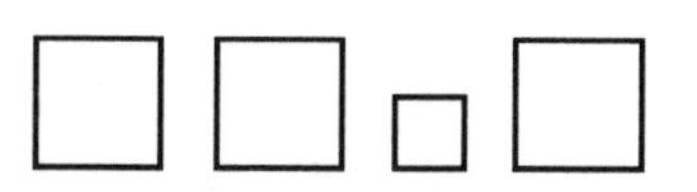 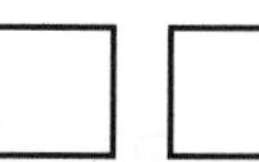 

Sequencing: Activity 9

Name________________________

Listen and then follow my directions.

1. Cut out the pictures of the boys. Then put them in order from smallest to biggest.

2. Cut out the pictures of the pencils. Then put them in order from tallest to shortest.

3. Cut out the pictures of the animals. Then put them in order from heaviest to lightest.

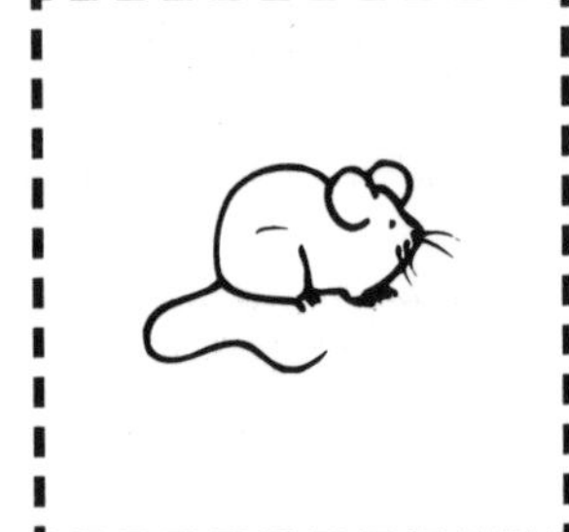

Sequencing: Activity 10

Name________________________

Listen to each story I read. Use the small boxes to number the pictures in the order they happened. Then you tell each story.

1. Carrie wanted to take her dog for a walk. First, she got the leash. Next, she put the leash on her dog. Last, Carrie took her dog outside and went for a walk.

2. First, Bobby wrote a letter to his aunt. Next, he put the letter in the envelope. Then he put a stamp on the letter and mailed it.

Name________________________

Look at each row of pictures. I'll tell you what is happening. Use the small boxes to number the pictures in the order they happened. Then you tell each story. Remember to use words like *first*, *next*, and *last* to tell your story.

1. Kevin is brushing his teeth.

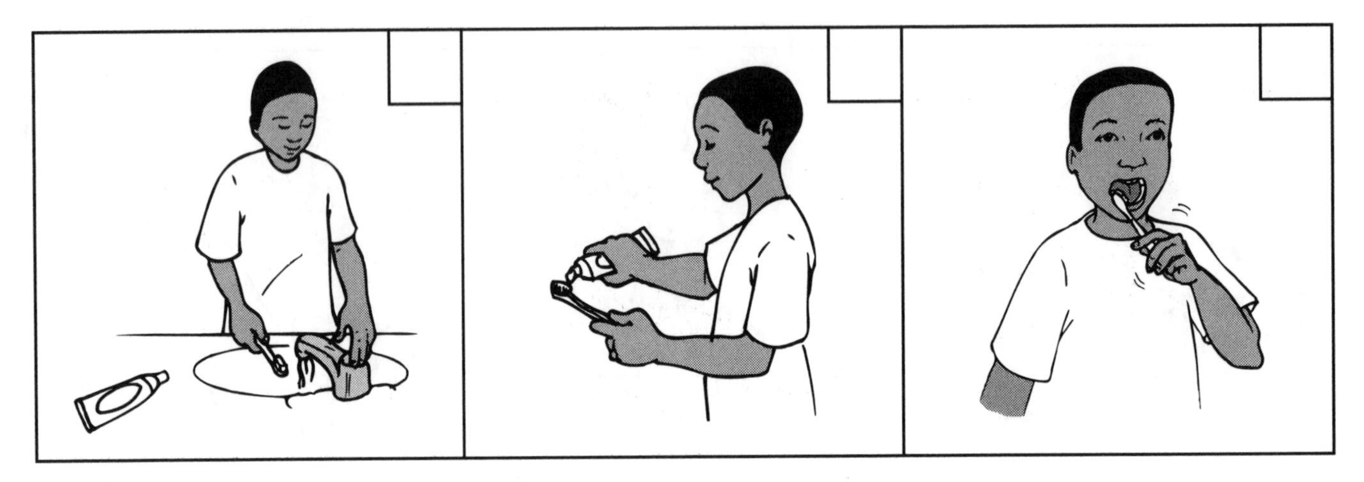

2. The bird is building a nest.

Sequencing: Activity 12

Name________________________

Look at each row of pictures. I'll tell you what is happening. Use the small boxes to number the pictures in the order they happened. Then you tell each story. Remember to use sequence words to tell your story.

1. Barry colored a picture for his dad.

2. Stephanie made a sandwich for lunch.

Sequencing: Activity 13

Name________________________

Cut out the pictures below and put them in the order they happened. Then tell a story about the girl. Use sequence words like *first*, *next*, and *last* to tell your story.

Name_______________________

Cut out the pictures below and put them in the order they happened. Then tell a story about the woman. Remember to use sequence words like *first*, *next*, and *last* to tell your story.

Sequencing: *Activity 15*

Name__________________________

The children are building a snowman. Cut out the pictures below and put them in the order they happened. In the empty box, draw a picture of what you think would happen last. Then tell a story about the children making a snowman. Remember to use sequence words like *first*, *next*, *then*, and *last* in your story.

Sequencing: Activity 16

Name______________________

The Millers are going camping. Cut out the pictures below and put them in the order they happened. In the empty box, draw a picture of what you think would happen last. Then tell a story about the Miller's camping trip. Remember to use sequence words in your story.

Name________________________

Listen to the stories I tell. Then retell each story.

1. Corey gets up early every morning. First, he gets dressed. Then he goes running.
2. Jenna wanted to go to her friend's house. First, Jenna put on her bike helmet. Then she rode her bike to her friend's house.
3. Putting puzzles together is fun. First, you put all the pieces together. Then you have a picture.
4. Sharon's aunt invited her to go swimming. Sharon was excited because she loved swimming. First, she packed her swimsuit and towel. Then she waited on the porch for her aunt.
5. Mark loves tomatoes. He decided to plant his own garden. When the tomatoes were ripe, he had enough to share with his whole family.
6. Tonya likes going to the library with her mom. During story hour, the librarian reads a story to the children. After story hour, the children always have cookies and juice.
7. Jeff let his dog Buster outside. When Jeff looked out the window, he saw Buster digging in the yard. Buster dug until he found his bone.
8. Tracy and her family spent the day at Wonder World. Tracy had fun, but she was tired by the end of the day. She was glad when it was time to go home.
9. Mr. Hope helped his children make a clubhouse. After the clubhouse was built, they all went to the hardware store and bought some paint and paintbrushes. When they got home, they painted the clubhouse. The children had fun working with their dad.
10. After the storm, there were leaves and branches all over the yard. First, Sue and Jason went outside and raked the yard. Next, they put the leaves into lawn bags. Last, they put the bags beside the curb. It took them a long time to finish.

Sequencing: *Activity 18*

Name____________________

▸ **Materials:** ball, table, chair, 3 blocks, book, paper, blue crayon, red crayon

Listen and then follow my directions. Wait until I finish talking before you begin.

1. First stand up. Then bounce the ball.
2. Hop two times. Then touch your nose.
3. Put one block on the floor. Next, put one block on the table.
4. Draw a blue line on the paper. Then draw a red line.
5. Put two blocks on the chair. Then put the paper on the floor.
6. Clap your hands, stomp your feet, and then sit down.
7. Pick up the book. Then put it on the table and open it.
8. Pick up the paper and put it on the table. Then draw a circle on the paper.
9. Say your name, turn around, and then sit down.
10. First, draw a big circle on the paper. Next, draw a square inside the circle. Last, color the square.
11. Before you pick up a block, pick up a crayon.
12. After you draw a circle on the paper, clap your hands twice.
13. Touch your stomach after you touch your leg.
14. Touch your head, but first, touch the floor.
15. Count to three after you open the book.

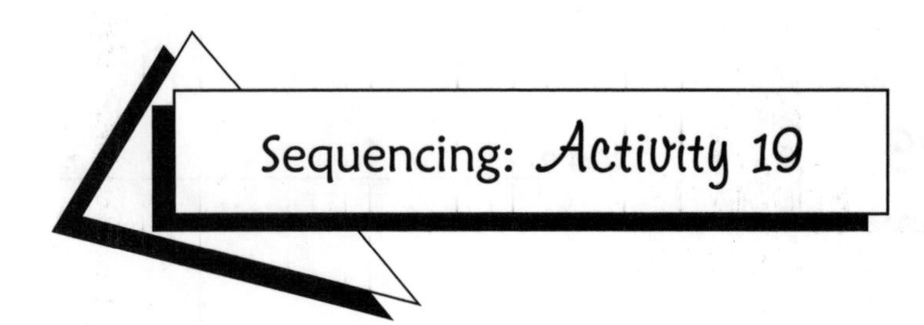

Name____________________

You do many different things every day. Some things you do in a certain order. Tell the steps you would follow to do each of the activities below. Remember to use sequence words like *first*, *next*, *then*, and *last* in your directions.

1. feed your dog
2. plant a flower
3. eat a banana
4. draw a picture
5. watch cartoons
6. blow your nose
7. brush your teeth
8. get ready for bed
9. make toast
10. play tag
11. make a phone call
12. play "Go Fish"
13. wash clothes
14. blow up a balloon
15. order food at a restaurant
16. unlock a door
17. play baseball
18. play a video game
19. make your bed
20. make a pizza

Sequencing: Activity 20

Name________________________

Stories are fun to listen to and to tell. I'm going to start a story. When I stop, I want you to tell the rest of the story.

1. Derek's favorite thing to do is play with his dog. Every day . . .

2. One day, Phil went to the park with his friends. When they got there, . . .

3. Tommy and his family went to the beach. The first thing Tommy did when he got there . . .

4. I once met a talking frog . . .

5. Dinosaurs lived many years ago. Dinosaurs are . . .

6. One night I dreamt that I was a . . .

7. Justine was a beautiful princess. She lived in a castle. Every day . . .

8. Greko was a friendly dragon. Once, a long time ago, . . .

9. Brody is getting a new pet rabbit. The first thing he will need to buy at the pet store is . . .

10. The trunk in the corner was a mystery to everyone. No one knew what was inside the trunk. One day, someone moved the trunk and found . . .

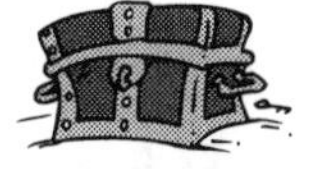

Name________________________

Look at the picture and answer my questions.

1. The Wakelands went to a movie. When they got to the theater, what do you think they did first?
2. What do you think they did right before they sat down?
3. What do you think the Wakelands will do after the movie?
4. Tell about a time you went to a movie. What did you do?
5. What is your favorite movie? Tell me more about it.

Sequencing: Activity 22

Name________________________

Look at the picture and listen as I tell you a story. Then answer my questions.

1. It's the last day of school at Jackson Elementary School. The school is having a special day. The students are playing games and having lots of fun! Two children are racing through cones. Point to the child who's in first place.
2. Look at the children running a race. Point to the child who is in second place. Now point to the child who is in third place.
3. Some of the children are at the ball toss. Which bucket is the ball going into?
4. Look at the children having a jump rope contest. Does the first child look tired? Which child does look tired, the second or the third child?
5. Pretend you're the teacher. Explain how to do the ball toss.
6. Tell about a time when you played games like the ones in the picture.

Name_______________________

Look at the picture and listen as I tell you a story. Then answer my questions.

The Bakers visited their relatives who live on a farm. One morning, the children asked their uncle if they could ride the horses. He said yes, but not until they helped with the chores. The first thing the children did was feed the cows. Then they fed the chickens. The last chore they did was sweep out the barn.

1. What did the children have to do before they could ride the horses?
2. What did the children do after they fed the cows?
3. What chore did the children do last?

When the children finished their chores, they were ready to ride. They helped their uncle catch the horses. Then they saddled the horses and went horseback riding. The children had a great day with their uncle!

4. When the children finished their chores, what did they do first?
   What did they do next?
5. Have you ever been to a farm? Tell about it.
6. Tell about the chores you do where you live.

Sequencing: Activity 24

Name________________________

Look at the picture and answer my questions.

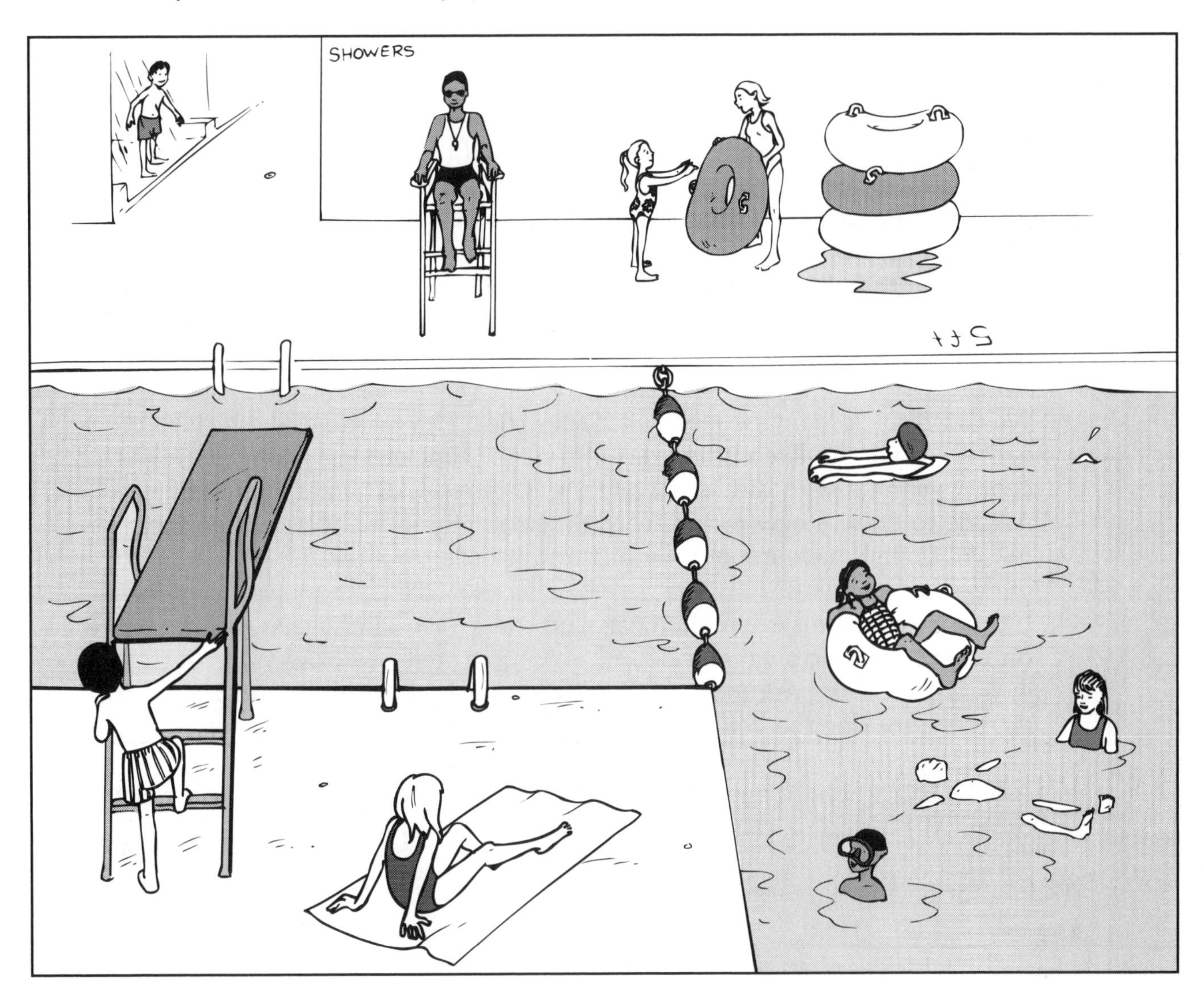

1. What should people do before they go into the swimming pool?
2. What is the girl in the flowered swimsuit doing first?
3. What do you think she'll do next?
4. What will the boy in the striped swimsuit do after climbing the ladder?
5. What do you think the people will do last?
6. Tell about a time when you went swimming.

Dear Family,

I've been learning how to sequence, or put things in order. You can help me practice at home by doing activities like the ones listed below. When we do the activities, remind me to use sequence words like *first*, *second*, *third*, *next*, *last*, *before*, and *after* to help me keep things in order.

- Read a short story to me. Then ask me to tell the story back to you. If you read a longer story, stop occasionally and ask me to tell you what has happened so far. Then ask me to tell you what I think will happen next.
- When you're finished reading the newspaper, we can cut apart a favorite cartoon series. Then I can put the pictures in order and tell you what happens.
- We can plant some grass seed in a paper cup. Have me draw a picture of each thing we do, like putting dirt in a paper cup, putting grass seed in the cup, covering it with dirt, and watering it. Then we'll watch the grass grow. Ask me to draw a new picture each time something changes. When the grass has grown tall, have me put my pictures in order and tell the story.
- Let me help you make simple meals and snacks like sandwiches, peanut butter on celery, and microwave popcorn. Ask me to tell you how to do each thing in the right order. Ask me to tell you how to do other things, too, like setting the table, making the bed, wrapping a birthday present, or tying my shoes.
- Ask me to tell you about the things I do each day, keeping them in the right order. We can use a calendar to talk about when things happen too.

Thanks for having fun with me and helping me learn!

Love,

____

Cause & Effect: Overview

The desire to understand cause and effect begins at an early age as toddlers repeatedly ask us "Why?" Although at times this can be frustrating and exhausting to us as adults, it is an important skill for children to master. The inability to make the connection between cause and effect can have life-long implications for some children. It can have an impact on the decisions we make about what we will and won't do, give us guidelines to follow when deciding the best way to do something, and help us understand how what happens will affect others.

The activities in this unit are designed to introduce basic cause and effect situations and provide your students with an opportunity to practice identifying and explaining cause and effect.

Using the Activity Pages

- Before beginning the activities in this unit, discuss the terms *cause* and *effect* with your students. Give some examples.
- When students are working on the activity pages, you may want to write a brief definition of *cause* and *effect* on the chalkboard to serve as a reminder such as "Cause = why something happened" and "Effect = what happened."
- Review the vocabulary on each page. Teach any words that may be new to your students.
- You may choose to reword the directions and/or questions on the activity pages using the terms *cause* and *effect*.
- Talk about a specific situation or picture from the activity pages and ask your students to tell you if it is a cause or an effect.
- Send the activity pages home for additional practice.

Expansion Activities

- Help your students identify cause and effect relationships in daily events. For example, what might happen if you forget to tie your shoes?

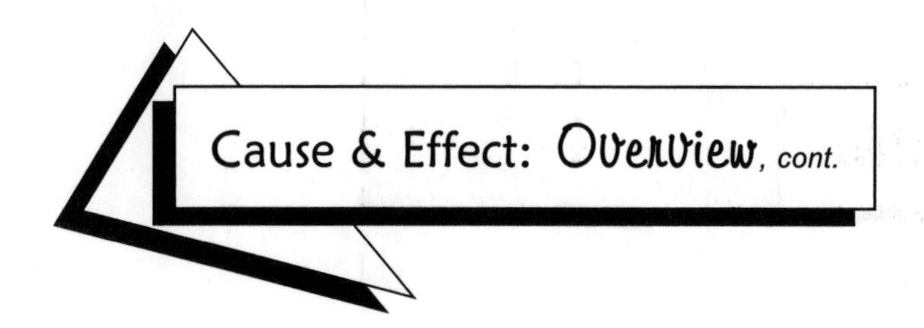

- Talk about rules and why they exist. Discuss the rules you find in different places like school, the playground, the ballpark, home, etc., and what happens if you break the rules. Explain the cause and effect relationships.

- As you read with your students, talk about the causes and effects found throughout the stories.

  After you have talked about the causes and effects in a story, retell the story, changing one or more of the "cause" details. Ask your students if the new details would change any of the effects that happened in the story. For example, in the story of *Goldilocks and the Three Bears*, tell your students that instead of going for a walk while their porridge cooled off, the bears had decided to take a nap. The effect of that change is that now the bears would be at home when Goldilocks arrived there.

- Help your students conduct some simple science experiments. Talk about the different causes and effects that occur.

Cause & Effect: Progress Chart

Name_______________________________

	Days / Trials			Comments
Activity 1				
Activity 2				
Activity 3				
Activity 4				
Activity 5				
Activity 6				
Activity 7				
Activity 8				
Activity 9				
Activity 10				
Activity 11				
Activity 12				
Activity 13				
Activity 14				
Activity 15				
Activity 16				
Activity 17				
Activity 18				
Activity 19				
Activity 20				
Activity 21				
Activity 22				
Activity 23				
Activity 24				

Name_______________________

Listen and then follow my directions.

1. Look at the first picture. What happened to Jason's shirt? Circle the picture that shows how it happened.

2. Look at the first picture. What happened to the window? Circle the picture that shows how it happened.

Cause & Effect: Activity 2

Name________________________

Listen and then follow my directions.

1. Look at the first picture of the girl. What happened to her knee? Point to the picture that shows how you think it happened.

2. Look at the first picture of the bike. What happened to the tire? Point to the picture that shows how you think it happened.

Cause & Effect: Activity 3

Name____________________________

Listen and then follow my directions.

1. Look at the first picture of the book. What happened to the page? Mark an **X** on the picture that shows how the page was torn.

2. Look at the first picture of the children. What are they doing? Mark an **X** on the picture that shows what made the children laugh.

Name____________________________

Listen and then follow my directions.

1. Look at the first picture of the snowman. What is happening to it? Circle the picture that shows what is causing it to melt.

2. Look at the first picture of the man. What happened to him? Circle the picture that shows how it happened.

Cause & Effect: Activity 5

Name________________________

Listen and then follow my directions.

1. Look at the children. Point to the picture that shows why they have to play inside.

2. Look at the boy. Point to the picture that shows how he broke his nose.

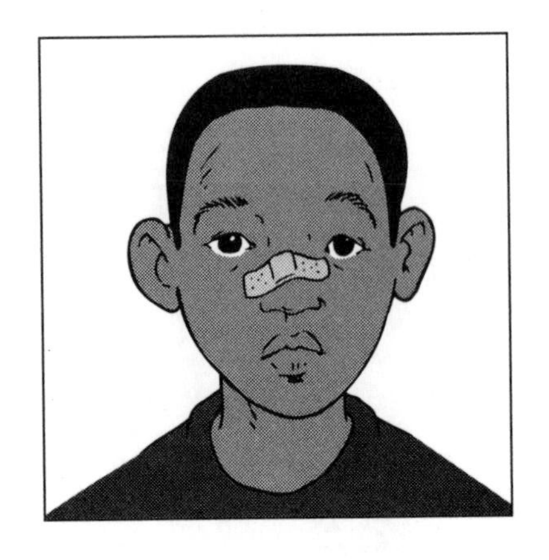

Cause & Effect: Activity 6

Name_______________________

Listen and then follow my directions.

1. Nathan's dad is upset. Mark an **X** on the picture that shows what happened to upset him.

2. Mrs. Meyers is frustrated. Mark an **X** on the picture that shows why she feels this way.

3. Caitlin doesn't want her dinner. Mark an **X** on the picture that shows why she doesn't want to eat.

Cause & Effect: Activity 7

Name________________________

Listen and then follow my directions.

1. Mark an **X** on the picture that shows what might happen on a windy day.

2. Mark an **X** on the picture that shows what might happen if you pulled the dog's tail.

3. Mark an **X** on the picture that shows what might happen if you bite hard candy.

Name________________________

Listen and then follow my directions.

1. Mark an **X** on the picture that shows what will happen to the ice cream if someone leaves the freezer door open.

2. Mark an **X** on the picture that shows what the cat will do if the neighbor's dog gets loose.

3. Mark an **X** on the picture that shows why the rancher had to build a new fence.

4. Mark an **X** on the picture that shows what might happen if you clean your room every week.

Name________________________

Listen and then follow my directions.

1. Dennis likes to hike in the woods. Circle the picture that shows what will happen if Dennis wears shorts while hiking.

2. Lisa is running barefoot on the sidewalk. Circle the picture that shows what might happen because Lisa isn't wearing any shoes.

3. Mrs. Halfman doesn't like to work in the garden. Circle the picture that shows what might happen if she doesn't water the garden.

4. The river is flooding. Circle the picture that shows what might happen if people don't put sandbags around the buildings near the river.

Cause & Effect: *Activity 10*

Name____________________________

Listen and then follow my directions.

1. Some animals got out of their pen. Mark an **X** on the picture that doesn't show how they got out.

2. Tommy is sad. Mark an **X** on the picture that doesn't show why he's sad.

3. Denise is allergic to cats. Mark an **X** on the picture that doesn't show what happens when Denise is around cats.

4. Joshua's grandparents gave him a new puppy. Mark an **X** on the picture that doesn't show why Joshua is afraid he'll have to give the puppy back.

Name________________________

Look at the pictures. Some pictures show things that happened, and other pictures show how the things happened. Draw a line to match each picture of what happened to how it happened. Then tell about each event.

What Happened

How It Happened

Name________________________

Look at the pictures. Some pictures show things that happened (effects), and other pictures show how the things happened (causes). Draw a line to match each picture of what happened to how it happened. Then tell about each event.

Effect

Cause

Cause & Effect: Activity 13

Name____________________________

Look at the pictures. Some pictures show things that happened (effects), and other pictures show how the things happened (causes). Draw a line to match each picture of what happened to how it happened. Then tell about each event.

Effect

Cause

Cause & Effect: Activity 14

Name________________________

Listen and answer my questions. Look at the pictures to help you think about your answers.

1. What might happen if you leave your toys on the stairs?

2. What might happen if you climb too high in a tree?

3. What might happen if you don't brush your teeth?

4. What might happen if you lose your house key?

5. What might happen if you leave your bike outside overnight?

6. What might happen if you forget to do your homework?

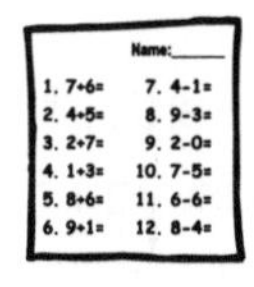

7. What might happen if you walk too far from home?

8. What might happen if you eat too much junk food?

Cause & Effect: *Activity* 15

Name____________________

Listen and answer my questions. Look at the pictures to help you with your answers.

1. Gwen wants to draw a picture, but her marker doesn't work. What do you think happened to the marker?

2. All of the people at the baseball game stood under the shelter. No one was on the field. Why do you think everyone was under the shelter?

3. Grace broke her arm when she was at the park. How do you think Grace broke her arm?

4. Curt saw a kite stuck in a tree. How do you think the kite got stuck in the tree?

5. There are tire marks in the front yard. What do you think happened?

6. When David looked outside, he saw that the grass was wet. How do you think it got wet?

7. Franklin is laughing. What do you think might have made him laugh?

8. Mr. Watson came home from work and found his newspaper scattered all over the front yard. What might have happened?

Cause & Effect: Activity 16

Name______________________________

Listen and answer my questions. Look at the pictures to help you think about your answers.

1. Imagine you helped your grandpa clean out the garage. How do you think that would make him feel?

2. Imagine you forgot to feed the dog. What do you think will happen?

3. Imagine you left your lunch money at home. What do you think will happen at lunchtime?

4. Imagine your family is supposed to go on a picnic, but your mom has to work late. What do you think will happen?

5. Imagine your brother called to say that he was going to be late, and you forgot to tell your dad. What do you think will happen?

6. Imagine you get to plan what your family will do on Saturday. When you wake up Saturday morning, it's raining. What effect will that have on what you will plan?

7. Imagine you broke the arm you use to write with. How do you think that would affect your writing?

8. Imagine you gave flowers to your teacher. What effect would that have on her day?

Cause & Effect: *Activity* 17

Name________________________

Listen to my questions and tell what you think might happen in each situation.

1. What will happen if you put water in the freezer?
2. What might happen if your ball rolls into the street?
3. What might happen if you forget to tie your shoes?
4. What might happen if you don't take your medicine?
5. What might happen if you drop something made of glass?
6. What might happen if your dad forgets to put gas in his car?
7. What will happen if you don't take a bath?
8. What might happen if someone doesn't wear a seatbelt?
9. What might happen if someone plays with matches?
10. What might happen if you step on a piece of glass?
11. What might happen if someone is walking his dog and lets go of the leash?
12. What might happen if your mom forgets to take the turkey out of the oven?
13. What will happen if you go outside when it's cold and don't wear a coat?
14. What might happen if you forget to set your alarm?
15. What might happen if you forget to tell your mom where you're going?

Name_______________________

Listen to my questions and tell what you think might have caused each situation.

1. Why might people hear sirens?
2. Why might the dog wag its tail?
3. Why might the children have to stay inside for recess?
4. Why might a child have to sit in the time-out chair?
5. Why might a baby cry?
6. Why might Cliff be too tired to get up in the morning?
7. Why might Paige bring treats to school?
8. Why might Kim have won a blue ribbon at the fair?
9. Why might someone go to the emergency room at the hospital?
10. Craig turned on the light switch, but no light came on. Why might this have happened?
11. Mrs. Smith went outside and called her dog, but the dog didn't come. Why might this have happened?
12. Chris went to get his permission slip for the field trip so his dad could sign it, but it wasn't in his backpack. Why might this have happened?
13. Tracy came out of school and found her bike on its side. Why might this have happened?
14. A car was on the side of the road. No one was in the car. Why might this have happened?
15. Betsy was playing outside in the grass. When she came inside, she had a rash. Why might this have happened?

Name____________________

Listen to the short stories I read and then answer my questions.

1. Jessie's grandmother's birthday is next week. Jessie and her mom went to the store to buy a birthday card.

   Where did Jessie and her mom go?
   Why did they need to go to the store?

2. Marcus was sad because he lost his favorite book.

   What was wrong with Marcus?
   Why did he feel sad?

3. Karen was walking home from school. All of a sudden she heard a dog barking. The barking scared Karen, so she ran the rest of the way home.

   What did Karen do at the end of the story?
   Why did Karen run home?

4. Drew wanted Carter to come outside and play. Carter's mom said he couldn't play because he was sick.

   Did Drew get to play with Carter?
   Why not?

5. Beth visited her dad at work. When they got to the factory area, it was very noisy. Beth had to wear special ear muffs just like all the workers.

   What did Beth have to wear?
   What do you think would happen if people in the factory area didn't wear the ear muffs?

Name____________________

Listen to the short stories I read and then answer my questions.

1. It was a hot summer day and the children were at the swimming pool. Everyone was playing and having fun. Suddenly, the lifeguard blew his whistle and yelled, "Walk!"

   What did the lifeguard do in the story?
   Why did he have to do that?

2. One day Emma was at the library doing homework. After a while, some of Emma's friends came and sat down with her. Soon the librarian came over and asked the girls to leave.

   What happened to the girls at the library?
   Why do you think that happened?

3. Carlos was excited because his grandparents were coming for a visit. Carlos had been waiting since early morning for them to arrive. After lunch, Carlos looked out the window and then ran to the door.

   What did Carlos do after he looked out the window?
   Why do you think he ran to the door?

4. It was winter and there was a bad snowstorm. Six inches of snow were already on the ground. There was so much snow that school was canceled. The children were happy because they wanted to go sledding.

   What did the children do at the end of the story?
   Why did they get to go sledding?

5. Students at Jackson Elementary School are raising money for the Save the Whales organization. They believe it's important to help keep the whales safe.

   Why are the students raising money?
   What might happen to the whales if they aren't protected?

Name____________________

Valerie's teacher asked her to tell about things that have happened that made her happy. Valerie thought about many things. Circle each picture that shows something that made Valerie happy. Then tell why you think it made her happy. Cross out the pictures of things that happened that wouldn't have made Valerie happy, and tell why you think that.

Name______________________________

Look at the picture and answer my questions.

1. The Malones are getting ready for dinner. Mrs. Malone told Abby to move away from the oven. Why do you think Abby's mom wanted her to move?

2. What does Mrs. Malone have on her hands? What would happen if she didn't use potholders?

3. Why is there steam coming from the pan on the stove? What will happen if the heat isn't turned down?

4. Mrs. Malone made just enough food for her family. What would happen if Abby's brother brings a friend home for dinner?

5. Have you ever been burned? Tell about what happened.

Name________________________

Look at the picture and answer my questions.

1. Look at the boy sitting on the ground. What do you think happened to him? How do you think he fell?
2. Look at the two other boys racing. One boy looks happy. What made him happy?
3. Look at the ramp. What might happen if the boys ride up the ramp without practicing?
4. The children are wearing helmets and pads. What might happen if they don't wear them?
5. What activities do you like to do? Do you need special equipment to do them?

Cause & Effect: Activity 24

Name________________________

Look at the picture and answer my questions.

1. Jason looked outside and saw his bike. Why do you think Jason got upset?
2. Mrs. Anderson was happy when she looked outside. She said, "Boy, we sure need this rain." Why do you think the rain made Mrs. Anderson happy?
3. Jason's grandpa lived with them. When Grandpa opened the door to get the newspaper, he wasn't very happy. Why do you think he was unhappy?
4. Look at the little children. What are they doing? Do you think they like the rain? Why?
5. Do you like it when it rains? Why? What are some good things that happen when it rains?

Dear Family,

I've been learning about cause and effect at school. I know that the *cause* is why something happened and the *effect* is what happened. You can help me better understand the relationship between cause and effect. Here are some ideas for activities that we can do.

We can talk about cause and effect as we do some simple experiments. Before we begin, tell me what we're going to do and ask me to tell you what I think will happen. Then, as we do the experiment, we can talk about what is happening. Here are some experiments we can try.

- What will happen when we pour bubble bath in the bathtub?
- What will happen if we fill a cup with water and put it in the freezer?
- What will happen if we put sugar into a glass of water and stir it?
- What will happen to an egg if we boil it in water?

You can also talk with me about things around our home that have a cause/effect relationship. For example, if you ask me to stop running inside, we could talk about why you don't want me to run. The fact that I might get hurt or break something would be the effect. The fact that I was running when I shouldn't be would be the cause.

We'll have fun learning together! Thank you for helping me!

Love,

____

Problem Solving: Overview

This unit is designed to help your students learn to use their language skills and awareness of everyday experiences to identify, understand, solve, and avoid problems they may encounter. As your students' skills develop, they will eventually begin to apply what they've learned to their own individual situations. Becoming good problem solvers will enable your students to be more successful in the classroom and in family and social settings.

Using the Activity Pages

- Review the vocabulary on each page. Teach any words that are new to your students.
- Simplify or increase the difficulty of the tasks by providing more or less information, or by rewording the directions or the questions.
- Reword questions to introduce new vocabulary. This will help your students realize that they may be asked for the same information in more than one way.
- As they complete the activity pages, encourage your students to share their own related experiences.
- Send the activity pages home for additional practice.

Expansion Activities

- Talk about the fact that many problems have more than one solution. Discuss how sometimes one solution may be better than another and why.
- Think of problems that may occur in your classroom, city, or town. Talk about different solutions to the problems. Then choose one of the problems and provide your students with additional information about the situation. Have them discuss whether the original solution is still the best choice or if a different solution would be better.
- As you read stories, stop periodically to talk about what problems have occurred. Ask your students to give ideas as to how they would solve the problems. When you have finished reading, have your students tell you how the problem was solved in the story.

- When a problem arises in your classroom, let your students help determine the solution. Write the situation on the chalkboard. Then have your students list possible solutions. Talk about the pros and cons of each solution. Let your students choose the solution that best fits the situation.

- Set aside time during the day to let each student tell about a problem he had or saw and how it was solved.

- Make up problem situations for your students to solve. For example, ask them to imagine what they would do in the following situations:

  You saw someone spitting gum on the sidewalk.

  Someone asked you to skip class.

  Your friends ask you to go with them to the mall, but you don't want to go.

  Your friends want you to go for a bike ride, but you don't know how to ride a bike.

  Your friend didn't get her homework done last night. She wants to look at your paper and quickly copy your answers.

Name______________________________

	Days / Trials			Comments
Activity 1				
Activity 2				
Activity 3				
Activity 4				
Activity 5				
Activity 6				
Activity 7				
Activity 8				
Activity 9				
Activity 10				
Activity 11				
Activity 12				
Activity 13				
Activity 14				
Activity 15				
Activity 16				
Activity 17				
Activity 18				
Activity 19				
Activity 20				
Activity 21				
Activity 22				
Activity 23				
Activity 24				

Problem Solving: Activity 1

Name________________________

Listen and then follow my directions.

1. It's time for Nathan to take his bath. Circle the pictures that show what Nathan needs.

2. Daphne needs to wrap a birthday present. Circle the pictures that show what she needs.

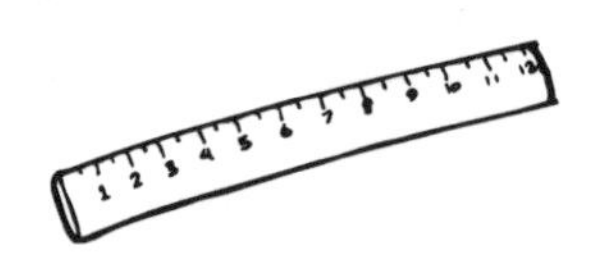
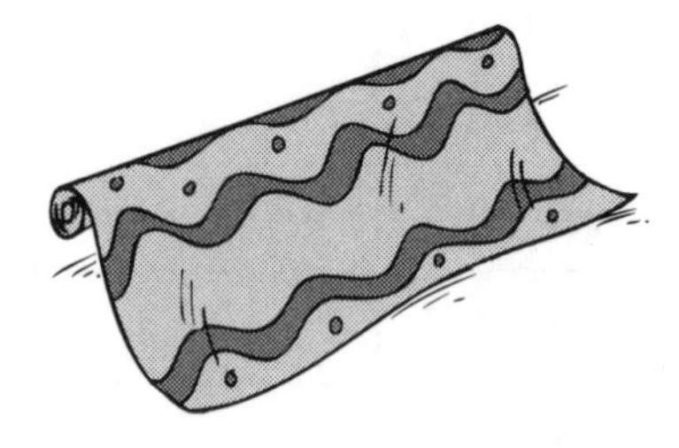

3. Carrie doesn't feel well. Circle the pictures that show what Carrie should do.

Problem Solving: *Activity* 2

Name________________________

Listen and then follow my directions.

1. Uncle Ed wants to take a picture of his sister's family. Circle the pictures that show what he needs.

2. James wants to make a sandwich. Circle the pictures that show what he needs.

3. Kelly wants to write a letter and send it to her aunt. Circle the pictures that show what she needs.

Name________________________

Look at the pictures and listen to what I say. Then answer my questions.

1. Carol wants to make a cake. What else does she need?

2. Clayton is ready to brush his teeth. What else does he need?

3. Danica is going to play softball. What else does she need?

4. Deanne wants to have a tea party with her friend. What else does she need?

Problem Solving: Activity 4

Name______________________

Listen and then follow my directions.

1. Kimberly spilled some milk on the floor. Mark an **X** on the picture that shows what Kimberly should do.

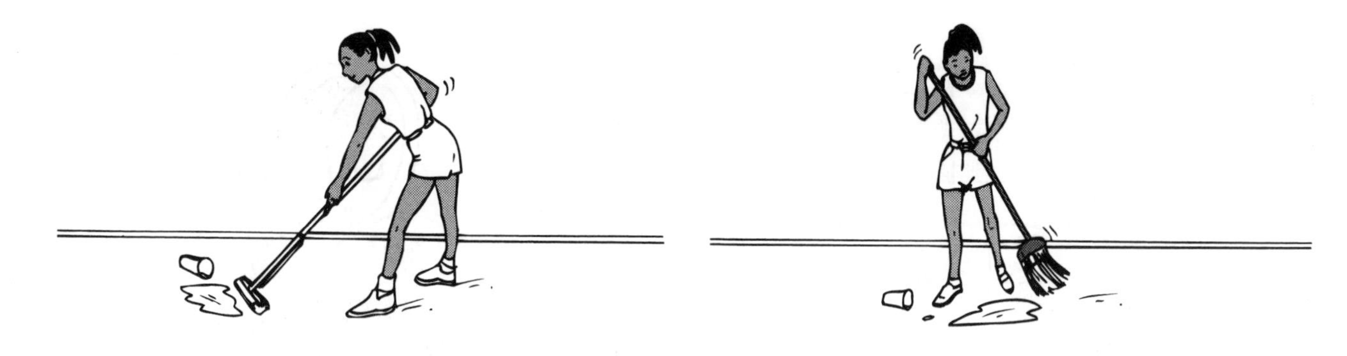

2. Jason wants to get a game from the top shelf, but he can't reach it. Mark an **X** on the picture that shows what Jason should do.

3. The sun was shining in Kayla's eyes while she was watching TV. Mark an **X** on the picture that shows what Kayla should do.

Problem Solving: *Activity* 5

Name______________________

Listen and then follow my directions.

1. Paula opened a book and found a torn page. Circle the picture that shows what she should use to fix it.

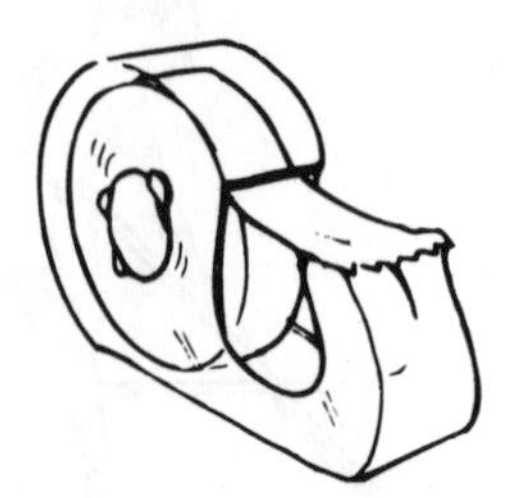

2. Jacob is unhappy because he can't go outside to play. Circle the picture that shows what Jacob should do.

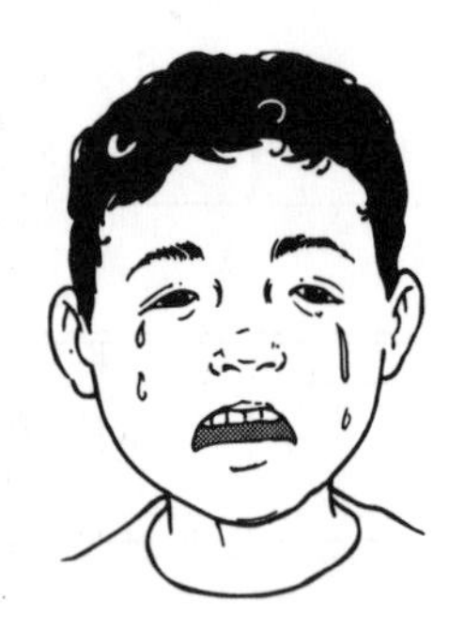

3. Courtney sees her little brother crawling toward the stairs. Circle the picture that shows what Courtney should do.

Name________________________

Listen and then follow my directions.

1. One of Dylan's toy cars rolled under the dresser. Mark an **X** on the picture that shows what Dylan should do.

2. Teresa broke her pencil lead. Mark an **X** on the picture that shows what Teresa should do.

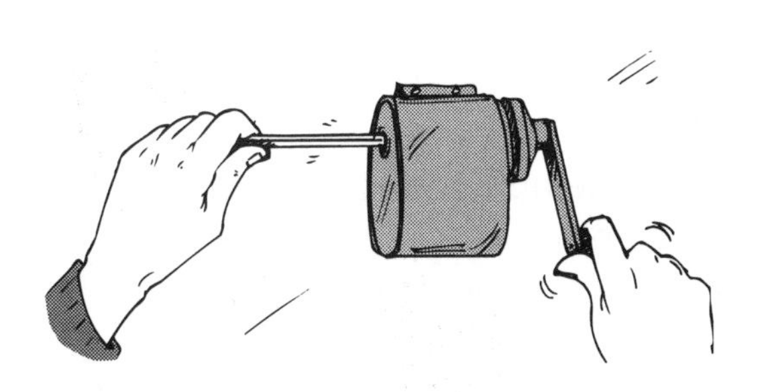

3. Stephen and Laura each want an apple for a snack, but there's only one apple left. Mark an **X** on the picture that shows what Stephen and Laura should do.

Problem Solving: Activity 7

Name________________________

Look at each picture and listen to what I say. Then tell me what the problem is.

1. Anita wants to ride her bike.

2. Mr. Philips fed his bird and then went outside.

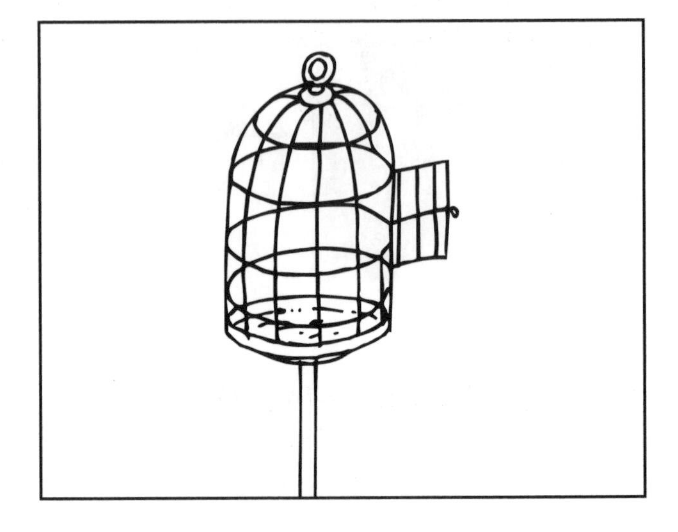

3. Ling borrowed a shirt from one of her friends.

4. Keesha needs to talk to her friend on the phone. She has a question about their homework assignment.

Problem Solving: Activity 8

Name______________________

Listen and then follow my directions.

1. Elena and her family were at the beach. When they went to get something to eat, Elena got separated from her family. Circle the picture that shows what Elena should do.

2. Ben accidentally broke a vase in the living room. Circle the picture that shows what Ben should do.

3. During recess, Kenesha saw someone being mean to a new student. Circle the picture of what Kenesha should do.

Name________________________

Look at the pictures and listen to what I say. Then answer my questions.

1. It's time for Noah's swimming lessons. What problem does Noah have? What should he do?

2. Mariah wants to color a picture for her grandpa. What problem does Mariah have? What should she do?

3. Drew is getting ready to leave for school. While he is tying his shoes, one of the laces breaks. What problem does Drew have? What should he do?

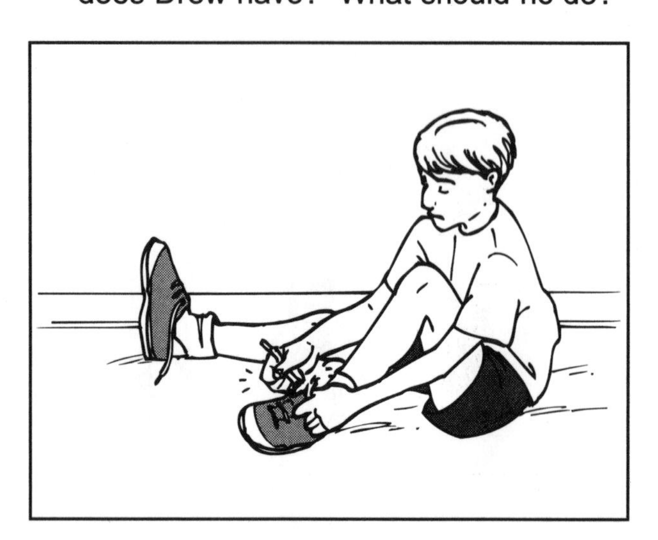

4. Amanda is trying to take her coat off, but she can't get it unzipped. What problem does Amanda have? What should she do?

Problem Solving: Activity 10

Name________________________

Look at the pictures. The ones on the left side of the page show problems. The ones on the right side of the page show things you would use to fix the problems. Draw a line from each problem to what you would use to fix it.

Problems	Solutions
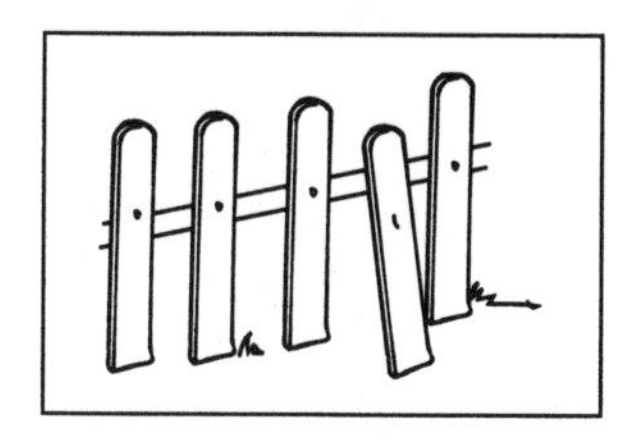	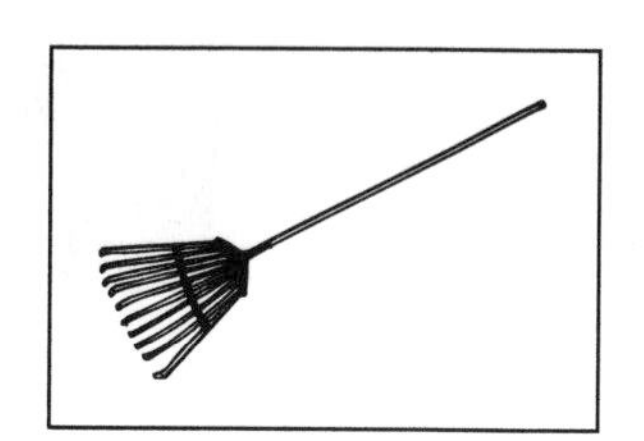
	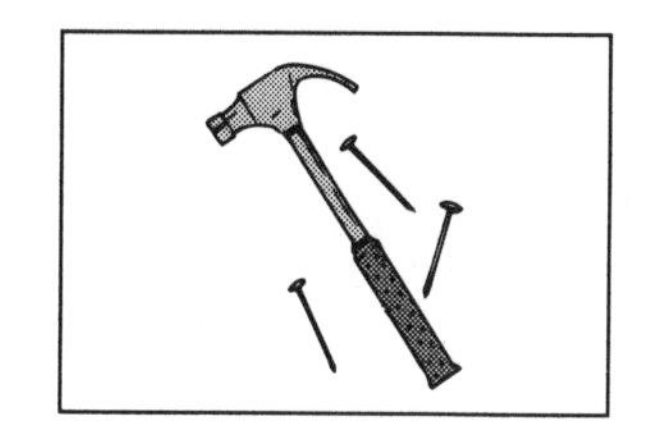
	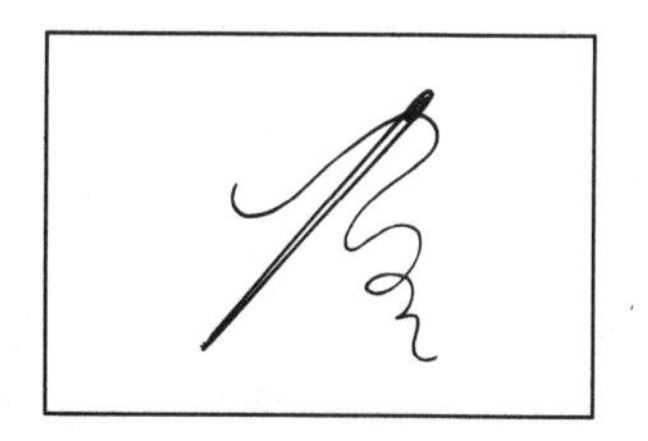

Name____________________

Look at the pictures and listen to what I say. Then follow my directions.

1. Hunter found a dead bug. He wanted to look at it closely. Circle the picture of what he could use to make the bug look bigger.

2. Elizabeth needed to measure ten things to finish her math assignment. Mark an **X** on the picture of what she would use for measuring.

3. Joan couldn't get the package of lunchmeat open. Draw a line under the picture of what she would use to open the package.

4. Forest lost his watch one night when he was camping. Draw a line through the picture of what he would use to look for his watch.

5. Colleen was going to take a long walk. She decided to take some water with her. Draw a box around the picture of what she would use to put her water in.

Problem Solving: Activity 12

Name______________________________

Look at each picture and tell what the problem is. Then tell what you would do to solve the problem.

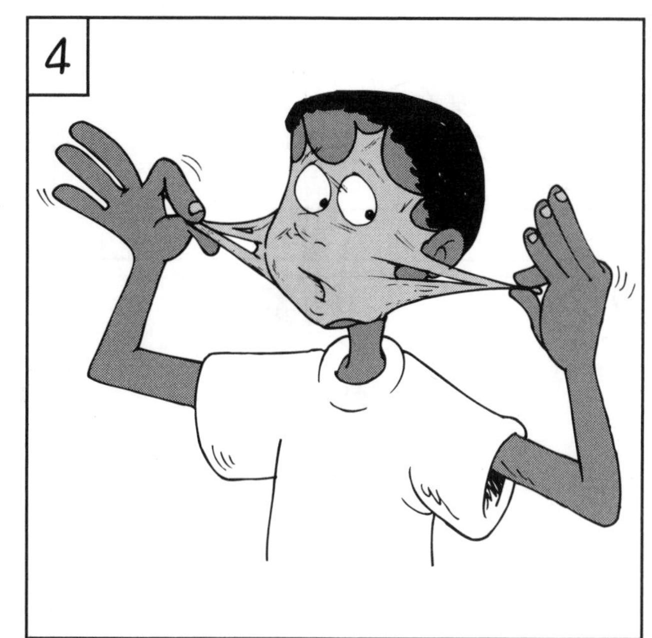

Name_______________________

Look at each picture and tell what the problem is. Then tell what you would do to solve the problem.

Name_______________________

Look at each picture and tell what the problem is. Then tell what could have prevented the problem from happening.

Problem Solving: *Activity* 15

Name________________________

Look at the pictures and listen to what I say. Then answer my questions.

1. Trent wants to go to his friend's house, but it's raining. Trent doesn't have a raincoat, so he decides not to go.

   What's the problem?

   What else could Trent use so he doesn't get wet?

2. Daniel and Troy decided to build a clubhouse. They wanted to use cardboard boxes, but they couldn't find any.

   What's the problem?

   What else could Daniel and Troy use to build a clubhouse?

3. Katie wants to buy her mom a birthday present, but she doesn't have any money. Katie asked her brother to loan her some money, but her brother said no.

   What is Katie's problem?

   What else could Katie do to get money to buy her mom a present?

4. Mitzi needs her science book, but she can't get her locker open. She decides to go to class without her science book.

   What is Mitzi's problem?

   What else could Mitzi have done?

Problem Solving: *Activity* 16

Name________________________

Look at the pictures below and listen to what I say. Then answer my questions.

1. Josh sat down to do his homework and realized he'd left his glasses at his friend's house. Josh called his friend and asked him to bring the glasses to school the next day.

   What was Josh's problem?

   How did Josh solve his problem?

   What else could Josh have done?

2. Maria is sad because her friend Amy is moving. She's afraid Amy will forget her. Maria and Amy have decided they will write each other one letter every week.

   What is Maria's problem?

   How does Maria solve her problem?

   What else could Maria and Amy do to stay in touch?

3. Sheila's friend invited her to a slumber party. Sheila had never spent the night away from home before so she decided not to go to the party.

   What was Sheila's problem?

   How did Sheila solve her problem?

   What else could Sheila have done?

Problem Solving: Activity 17

Name______________________________

Look at the pictures below and listen to what I say. Then follow my directions.

1. Kyle wants to read the book *Charlotte's Web* by E.B. White, but he doesn't have it. Name two things Kyle could do.

2. Mr. Miles needs to get some medicine for his cold. Name two things Mr. Miles could do.

3. Claudia wants soup for lunch but she doesn't have any. Name two things Claudia could do.

4. Mr. Dexter broke his leg and can't drive. Unfortunately, he has a lot of work to do and needs to go to work. Name two things Mr. Dexter could do.

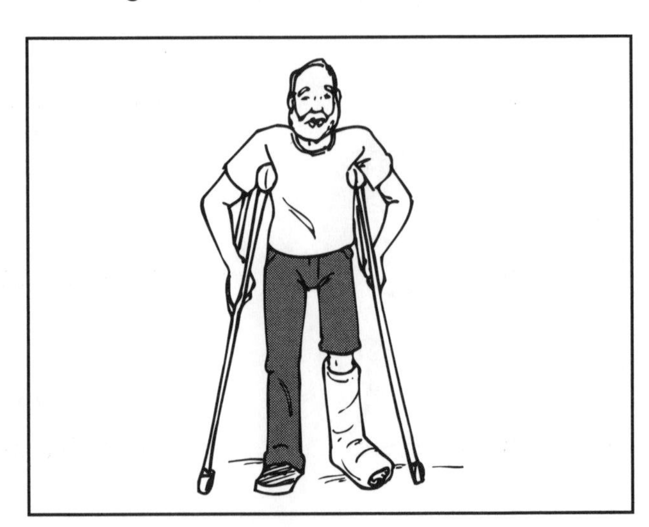

Problem Solving: *Activity 18*

Name________________________

Listen and answer my questions. Look at the pictures to help you with your answers.

1. Where would you go if you needed to buy cough medicine?

2. Where would you go if you wanted to buy a newspaper?

3. Where would you go if you needed to buy a birthday present?

4. Where would you go if you wanted to buy a lawnmower?

5. Where would you go if you had a toothache?

6. Where would you go if you needed to buy bread and milk?

7. Where would you go if your dog was sick?

8. Where would you go if you had trouble seeing the chalkboard?

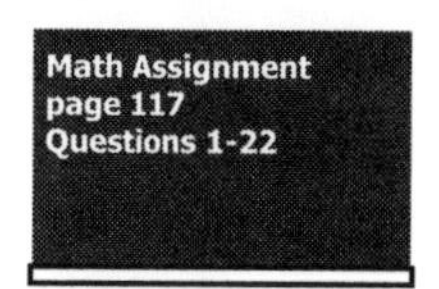

Name____________________

Listen to each situation and tell me what you would do.

1. What would you do if you were sick at school?
2. What would you do if you needed to find a phone number?
3. What would you do if you wanted to know the date?
4. What would you do if you found a ball in your yard that wasn't yours?
5. What would you do if you got home from school and realized you had left your backpack on the bus?
6. What would you do if you saw the neighbor's dog was loose?
7. What would you do if you didn't hear the homework assignment?
8. What would you do if you spilled juice on the carpet?
9. What would you do if you lost your key and couldn't get into your house?
10. What would you do if you were home alone and the electricity went out?
11. What would you do if you looked outside and saw a raccoon in your garbage?
12. What would you do if your sister was baby-sitting you, and she wouldn't let you invite a friend over?
13. What would you do if you needed to ask your dad a question, but he was on the phone?
14. What would you do if you were walking down the street and you saw smoke?
15. What would you do if you were home alone and someone knocked on the door?

Name____________________

Listen to each situation and tell me what you would do.

1. What would you do if you saw someone cheat on a spelling test?
2. What would you do if you didn't know the rules of a game your friends were playing?
3. What would you do if you were supposed to call a friend for an assignment you missed, but your friend wasn't home?
4. What would you do if you were reading a book and didn't know the meaning of a word?
5. What would you do if you were supposed to walk the dog, but you couldn't find the leash?
6. What would you do if you knew who found someone else's money, but the person didn't give it back?
7. What would you do if you were going to be home later than you said you'd be?
8. What would you do if you lost a note from your teacher about a special school event?
9. What would you do if you saw a stranger breaking into your neighbor's garage?
10. What would you do if you were in the bathroom at school and heard the fire alarm?
11. What would you do if someone asked you to steal something?
12. What would you do if your friend got in trouble for something you did?
13. What would you do to help a friend who was sad because her parents just divorced?
14. What would you do if you were at the park and saw someone sitting alone crying?
15. What would you do if you found out your friend smoked cigarettes?

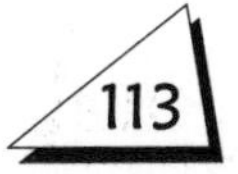

Problem Solving: Activity 21

Name_______________________

Look at the picture and answer my questions.

1. There are a lot of people watching the parade. The little girl in the striped shirt is with her dad. She can't see over the people in front of her. What could she do so she can see the parade?

2. The car that's pulling the float with the parade queen on it has broken down. What problem does that cause? What should the person driving do?

3. Look at the bumblebee balloon. What problem do you see? What should the people holding the balloon do?

4. The parade is only half over and it's very cloudy. What might happen? What problem would rain cause? What do you think the people watching the parade should do? What do you think the people in charge of the parade should do?

5. Have you ever been to a parade? Tell about it.

Problem Solving: Activity 22

Name_______________________

Look at the picture and answer my questions.

1. Lauren went to the museum. Before she could go inside, she had to throw away her drink. Why do you think the museum doesn't allow people to bring food or drinks inside?

2. The first thing Lauren saw was a big dinosaur skeleton. A sign beside the dinosaur says PLEASE DO NOT TOUCH. Why do you think the sign is there? What do you think would happen to someone who touched the dinosaur?

3. Lauren also saw a mummy. It's in a glass case. Why do you think the mummy is in a glass case?

4. Look at the rest of the picture. What is another way the museum workers stop people from touching items in the museum?

5. Look at the room that says Children's Museum. What things do you see? There aren't any DO NOT TOUCH signs. Why do you think the museum has the children's room?

6. Have you ever been to a museum? What was it like?

Name_______________________

Look at the picture and answer my questions.

1. Nelson and Wes went to play miniature golf. When they got there, Nelson realized he had only brought $5. What problem did he have? What do you think he should do? What could Nelson have done before he left home to avoid the problem?

2. Wes loaned Nelson some money, and the boys picked up their balls and clubs. On the first hole, Nelson hit his ball into the water. What do you think he should do?

3. When Nelson and Wes finished the first hole, they had to wait. The little boy ahead of them had lost his ball. Where do you think the ball might be? It's caught under the windmill. How do you think the boy will get the ball?

4. What other problems could happen to someone while playing miniature golf?

5. Have you ever played miniature golf? Tell about it.

Name________________________

Look at the picture and answer my questions.

1. What is the weather like? What problems can that cause?
2. The people who own the grocery store want people to be careful. What did they do to warn people about being careful on the ice and snow?
3. Look at the picture again. What other problems do you see? Tell me about them. What do you think the people in each situation should do?
4. What are some other problems that could happen at the grocery store or in the parking lot? Think about things that aren't in the picture.
5. What is the weather like where you live? What problems can that cause?

Dear Family,

I've been learning how to solve problems. You can help me practice at home by doing activities like the ones below. I'll learn to think about things and be a better problem solver.

Before we do an activity like coloring, making cookies, or doing the dishes, ask me to tell you all the things we'll need. For example, if we're going swimming, we would need swimsuits, towels, and sunscreen.

When we're reading stories, stop and ask me about a problem a character is having. For example, if we're reading *The Three Little Pigs*, ask me to tell you what problems the pigs have. Then ask me to tell you how the pigs solved their problems.

When you see something wrong, ask me to tell you why it's a problem. Then ask me what should be done. For example, if the windows are open and it's starting to rain, we could close them.

Make up problem situations and ask me to solve them. Here are some ideas:

- I want to watch a special program on TV, but someone else is already watching his favorite show. What could I do?
- I'm having trouble putting a puzzle together. What could I do?
- I borrowed something from a friend and lost it. What could I do?

Thank you for practicing with me!

Love,

____

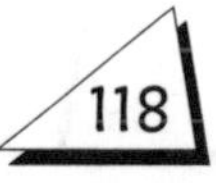

People have opinions on just about everything, from relatively simple concepts like which restaurant has the best pizza to more complex ideas such as world politics. Many times each day, we share our opinions as part of our day-to-day communications with others.

Unfortunately, students whose language skills are weak often have difficulty expressing their opinions. This may be one factor that contributes to the level of success these students have with conversational and written language skills. The activities in this unit are based on common, everyday situations and are designed to give your students practice with the important language skill of expressing opinions.

Using the Activity Pages

- Before beginning the activities in this unit, talk about what opinions are. Explain that when you give an opinion there is no right or wrong answer.
- Review the vocabulary on each page. Teach any words that may be new to your students.
- Discuss things that might influence opinions, like personal experiences, likes and dislikes, what friends and family think, etc.
- Expand on the situations presented on the activity pages. Involve your students by asking them to share personal experiences that might be similar.
- Talk about the words *agree* and *disagree*. These are introduced in later activities.
- Send the activity pages home for additional practice.

Expansion Activities

- Explain that everyone is entitled to his own opinion, and help students understand that it's okay to have a different opinion from someone else. You might also have each student identify situations in which his opinion is all that matters. For example, when choosing which kind of ice-cream cone to get, not everyone has to have the same flavor.

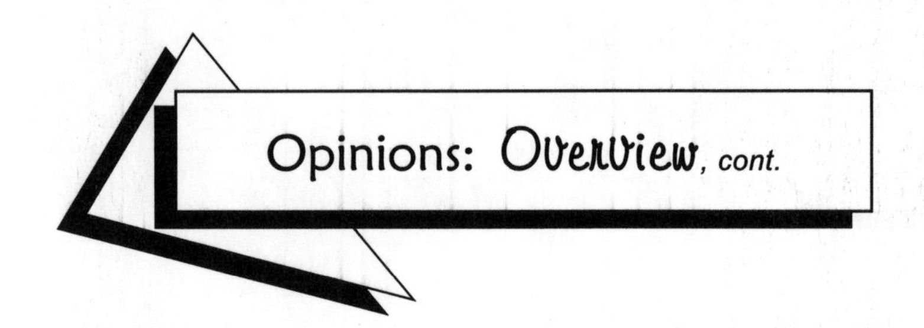

- If your students are ready, talk about the impact people's opinions can have on decisions that are made. Explain the idea of "the majority rules." Depending on the age and level of your students, illustrate this concept by talking about things such as which TV program to watch or issues like who will be the next president. Introduce the concept that even though you have an opinion, things may not turn out the way you want them to.

- Provide opportunities for your students to give their opinions on classwork. For example, give them two or more choices of a new story and ask for their opinions about which one the class should read. Remind them that the majority rules.

- Have your students make charts to show how people's opinions are different. For example, they could find out how many people have the same favorite color, flower, sport, or type of music.

Name________________________

	Days / Trials			Comments
Activity 1				
Activity 2				
Activity 3				
Activity 4				
Activity 5				
Activity 6				
Activity 7				
Activity 8				
Activity 9				
Activity 10				
Activity 11				
Activity 12				
Activity 13				
Activity 14				
Activity 15				
Activity 16				
Activity 17				
Activity 18				
Activity 19				
Activity 20				
Activity 21				
Activity 22				
Activity 23				
Activity 24				

Opinions: Activity 1

Name________________________

Some people are picky eaters. Look at the pictures below and circle the foods you think are good to eat.

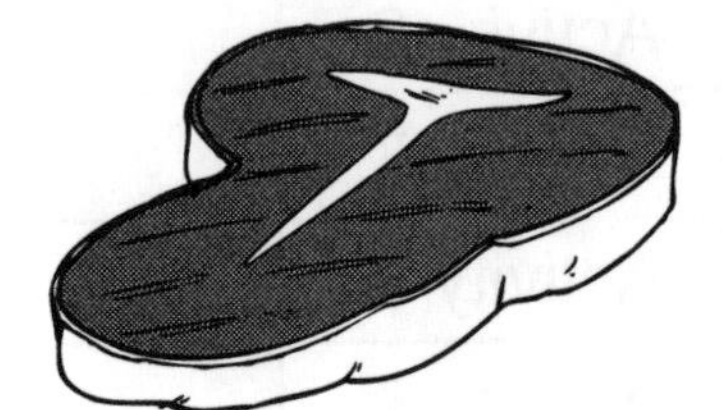

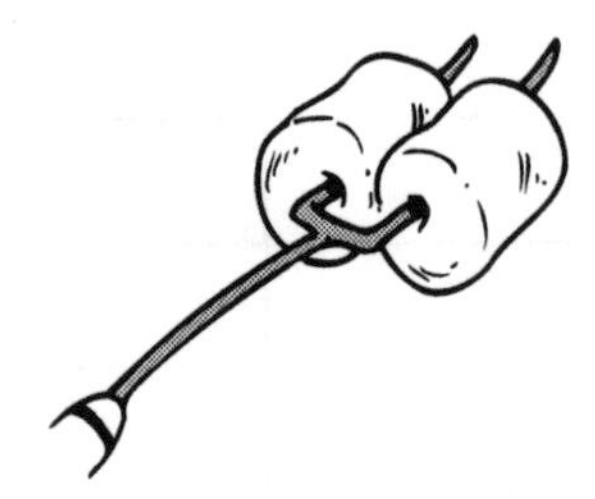

Opinions: Activity 2

Name____________________________

Look at the pictures below. Circle the pictures of the things you like to play with. Tell why you like to play with them.

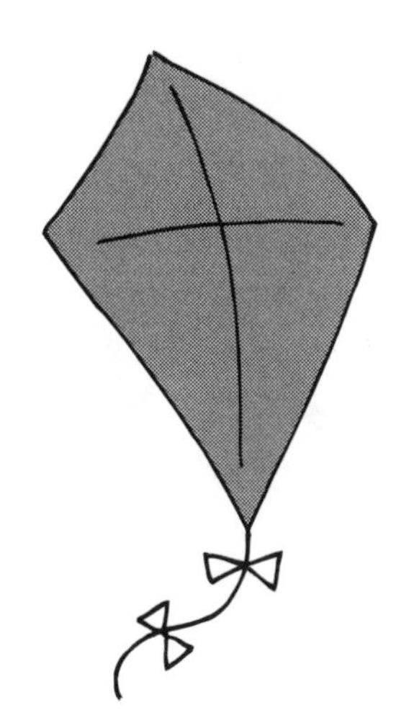

Opinions: Activity 3

Name________________________

Look at the pictures below. Some of the items are things you would keep, and some are things you would throw away. Mark an **X** on the things you would not keep. Then tell why you would throw these things away.

Opinions: Activity 4

Name_______________________________

There are a lot of rides at an amusement park. Look at the pictures below. Circle the rides you like to go on. Tell why you like them. Then tell why you don't like to go on the other rides.

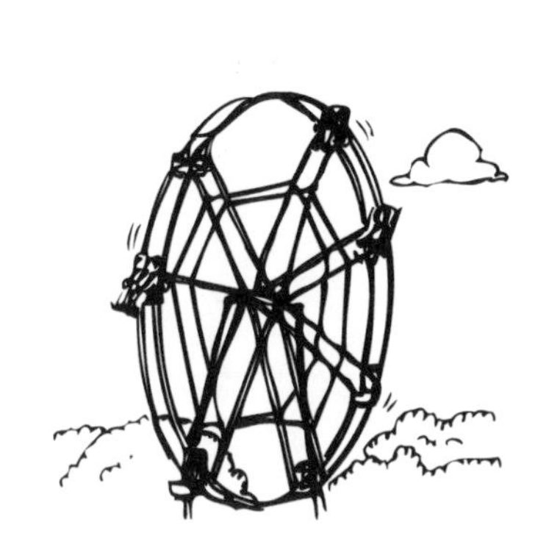

Opinions: Activity 5

Name______________________________

Look at the pictures below. Circle the animals you think would make good pets. Tell why you think so. Then tell why you think the other animals wouldn't make good pets.

Opinions: Activity 6

Name________________________

Listen to each question I ask. Then underline the picture that shows which thing you would rather do. Tell why.

1. Which would you rather do before you go to bed, listen to music or watch TV?

2. Which sport would you rather play, baseball or soccer?

3. Which would you rather do to get clean, take a bath or a shower?

4. Which one would you rather do on a hot day, go swimming or play in the sprinkler?

Opinions: Activity 7

Name____________________________

Listen to each question I ask. Then underline the picture that shows which thing you would rather use. Tell why.

1. Which one would you rather use to glue pieces of paper together?

2. Which one would you rather use to take your lunch to school?

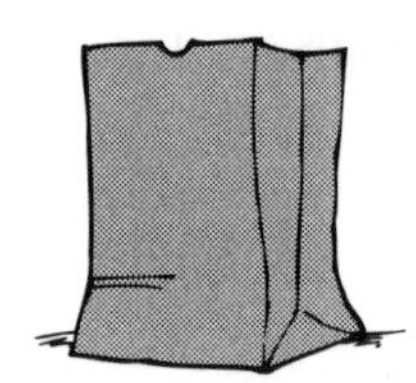

3. Which one would you rather use to water a garden?

4. Which one would you rather use to make a picture?

Opinions: Activity 8

Name________________________

Look at the pairs of pictures below. Circle the activity that you think is more fun to do. Then tell why you think so.

Opinions: *Activity 9*

Name____________________

Look at the pictures of things to eat and drink. Circle the picture in each row of what you like best. Then tell why.

Row 1

Row 2

Row 3

Row 4

Row 5

Opinions: Activity 10

Name____________________________

Listen to each question I ask. Then mark an **X** on the picture that shows which thing you would rather do. Tell why.

1. Which activity would you rather do with your friends?

2. Which toy would you rather play with?

3. Which activity would you rather do at the park?

4. Which activity would you like to do on a rainy day?

5. Which chore would you rather do to help at home?

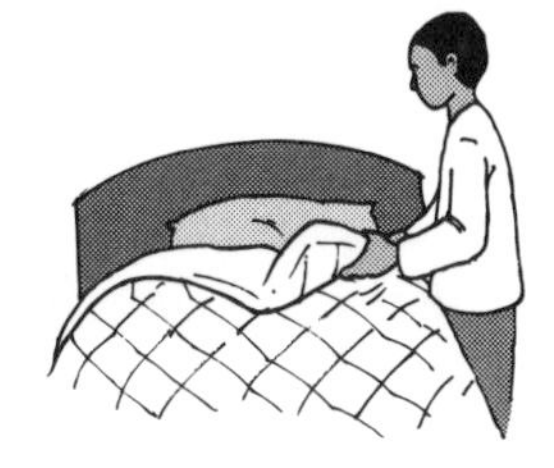

Opinions: Activity 11

Name________________________

Look at the pictures and follow my directions. Then tell why you chose each item.

1. Circle the picture of what you would rather eat for breakfast.

2. Mark an **X** on the picture of what you would rather eat for lunch.

3. Circle the picture of what you would rather eat for dinner.

4. Mark an **X** on the picture of what you would rather eat for a snack.

Name______________________

Look at the pictures. I'm going to tell you about them. Then answer my questions.

1. Katie is opening her birthday present. Do you think she likes what she received? Why? What do you think Katie should say?

2. Tiffany thinks the library is a good place to study. Do you agree? Sometimes Tiffany sits with a friend. Do you think this is a good place for the girls to talk? Why? Where else could they go to talk?

3. Grant is taking his shoes and socks off. Do you think it's okay for Grant to do that? Why?

Opinions: Activity 13

Name______________________________

Look at the pictures. I'm going to tell you about them. Then answer my questions.

1. Mrs. Taylor has a rule that there is no talking in her classroom. Do you think that's a good rule? Why?

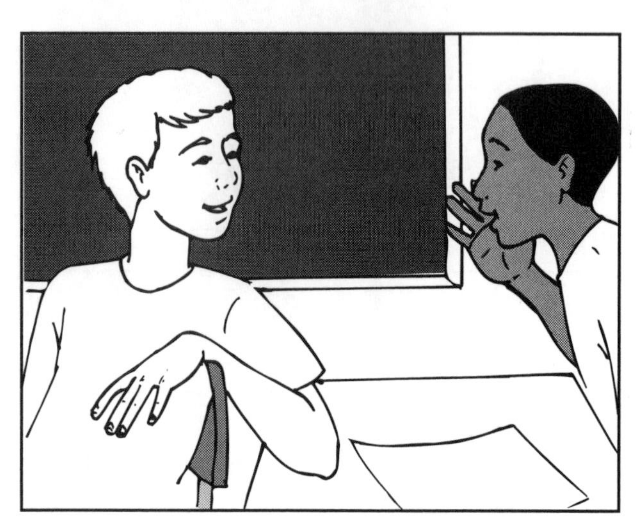

2. One of the rules at the swimming pool is No Running. Do you think this is a good rule? Why?

3. At the ballpark, climbing on the fence is not allowed. Do you think this is a good rule? Why?

4. You have to wear shoes and a shirt when going into a restaurant. Do you think that's a good rule? Why?

Opinions: Activity 14

Name______________________

Look at the pictures. I'm going to tell you about them. Then answer my questions.

1. Karen is going to paint her bedroom. She wants it to look bright and cheery. What color do you think she should paint it? Why?

2. Megan and Nicole want to surprise their mom by doing something nice for her. What could they do? Why do you think they should do that?

3. Nick was supposed to do his chores before going to his friend's house. When it was time to leave, he wasn't finished yet. Do you think Nick should be able to go to his friend's house? Why?

4. Donaven wants to stay up late to visit with his cousins from out of town, but he has to go to school the next day. Do you think he should be allowed to stay up past his bedtime? Why?

Name______________________

Listen to my questions and tell me what you think.

1. Do you think riding a bike is easy or hard? Why?
2. Do you like having a clean room or a messy room? Why?
3. Do you like watching long or short movies. Why?
4. Do you like getting up early or sleeping late? Why?
5. Do you like eating snacks that are crunchy or soft? Why?
6. Do you think playing tag is fun or boring? Why?
7. Would you rather play inside or outside? Why?
8. Would you rather have a big or small dog? Why?
9. Would you rather eat sour or sweet candy? Why?
10. Would you rather eat pizza with thick or thin crust? Why?
11. Would you rather sit on a soft or hard chair? Why?
12. Would you rather play cards or a board game? Why?
13. Would you rather watch cartoons or a movie? Why?
14. Would you rather eat Jell-O or yogurt? Why?
15. Would you rather go fishing or fly a kite? Why?

Name________________________

Listen to my questions and tell me what you think.

1. Would you rather eat an apple or drink apple juice? Why?
2. Do you like to sleep with your bedroom door open or closed? Why?
3. Do you like to eat hot cereal or cold cereal? Why?
4. Would you rather have soup or a salad with your lunch? Why?
5. Would you rather go for a ride on a boat or a train? Why?
6. If you had bunk beds, would you rather sleep on the top bunk or the bottom bunk? Why?
7. Would you rather be first or last when playing a game? Why?
8. Who should wash the dishes at your home, you or someone else? Why?
9. Do you think people should laugh or cry at a sad movie? Why?
10. Is it right or wrong to tell a lie? Why?
11. Would you rather read a book silently or aloud? Why?
12. Where would you like to go on vacation, to the mountains or to the beach? Why?
13. Should you eat something that has fallen on the floor? Why?
14. If you find something that doesn't belong to you, should you keep it or give it back? Why?
15. Do you think books about outer space are better than books about dinosaurs? Why?

Opinions: Activity 17

Name________________________

Listen to my questions and tell me what you think.

1. Should you look both ways before you cross the street? Why?
2. Should you play outside after dark? Why?
3. Should people wear helmets when they ride bikes? Why?
4. Should you pick up something you find on the ground? Why?
5. Should small children use scissors? Why?
6. Should you wear mittens and hats when it's cold outside? Why?
7. Should you hold on to the railing when you walk down steps? Why?
8. Should you talk to strangers? Why?
9. Should you tell someone if you're going outside to play? Why?
10. Should people wear seatbelts? Why?
11. Should small children be allowed to ride roller coasters? Why?
12. Should dogs be allowed to run loose? Why?
13. Should you fix the lock on your door if it breaks? Why?
14. Should people ride scooters in the street? Why?
15. Should you pick up broken glass with your bare hands? Why?

Opinions: Activity 18

Name_______________________

Listen to what I say and tell me if you agree or disagree. Then tell me why.

1. Chocolate is the best kind of ice cream. 

2. Cats are friendlier than dogs. 

3. Eating candy is bad for your teeth. 

4. Taking turns is important when playing a game. 

5. It's okay to laugh when someone gets hurt. 

6. Children should go to school on Saturday. 

7. Carrots taste great! 

8. Magicians are fun to watch. 

Opinions: Activity 19

Name________________________

Listen to what I say and tell me if you agree or disagree. Then tell me why.

1. All children should go to bed at 8:00 p.m.
2. Grasshoppers are hard to catch.
3. Baseball is the best sport.
4. People should eat fruit every day.
5. Everyone should have a dog.
6. Puppet shows are fun to watch.
7. It's fun to visit an aquarium with dolphins and whales.
8. A book is a good present to give someone.
9. It's important to brush your teeth every day.
10. Children should be allowed to have pets at school.
11. Children should have to help clean the house.
12. Broccoli should be served at least three times a week.
13. Teachers should not give students homework.
14. You should wash your hands after using the rest room.
15. Children should not watch TV for more than one hour a day.

Name______________________

I'm going to ask you some questions. There are no right or wrong answers. Just tell me what you think and why.

1. What is the best movie you've ever seen?
2. What is your favorite toy?
3. Where is your favorite vacation spot?
4. When you spend the night at a friend's house, should you carry your things in a backpack or suitcase?
5. If you were going on a long vacation, would you rather drive or fly?
6. Would you rather go hiking or play tennis?
7. If you break something that belongs to someone else, what do you do?
8. What should you do if your mom tells you to clean up but you still want to play?
9. If someone pushes you down, what do you do?
10. Is loud music better to listen to than soft music?
11. Should students be allowed to chew gum at school?
12. Should homework always be finished before you can go outside to play?
13. If you stay home sick from school, should you be allowed to go anywhere else?
14. Do you think you should be allowed to have dessert if you don't finish your dinner?
15. Should everyone have to stay in from recess if only two children are in trouble for talking?

Opinions: Activity 21

Name________________________

Look at the picture of McKinley School Fun Night and answer my questions.

1. Leigh likes clowns. She thinks they're funny. What do you think? Why?
2. Dan doesn't like the ring toss game. He thinks it's too hard. Do you think the ring toss is a hard game? Why?
3. Al doesn't want to go through the Mystery Mansion. He thinks it's too scary. Do you think it would be scary? Why?
4. Linda won a prize at the basketball free throw. She can't decide which prize to choose. Which one would you choose? Why?
5. What would you do first if you were at this Fun Night? Why?

Opinions: Activity 22

Name________________________

Look at the picture of the day care and answer my questions.

1. There's a toy stuck under the couch. Should the little girl try to move the couch by herself or ask for help? Why?

2. Imagine you saw the person who colored on the wall. Should you tell someone? Why?

3. Joe and Libby are playing with the cars. They're arguing about who should get to play with the sports car. Joe had it first. Do you think Libby should be allowed to take the sports car? Why? What else could the children do?

4. What do you think the children should do when they're finished playing?

Name________________________

Look at the picture of the fast-food restaurant and answer my questions.

1. Imagine you want to get something to eat. Would you wait in line at this restaurant or go somewhere else? Why?
2. The cashier gave the man at the counter the wrong amount of change. What do you think the man should do? Why?
3. The people sitting at the table got the wrong food. Should they eat it anyway or take it back? Why?
4. Imagine you were eating at this restaurant and you saw something spilled on the floor. Should you clean it up or tell someone who works there? Why?
5. Where is your favorite place to eat? Why do you like to eat there?

Name____________________

Look at the picture of the park and answer my questions.

1. The owner of the dog is letting the dog run loose in the park. Do you think the dog should be off of its leash? Why?

2. Two children are wading in the fountain. Do you think it's a good idea to let them do that? Would you like to wade in the fountain?

3. Someone littered. Do you think someone should pick up the trash and throw it in the garbage can or just let it blow away?

4. The man doesn't realize he dropped his wallet. Should the woman on the bench leave the wallet on the ground or return it to the man who dropped it? What else could the woman do with the wallet? What would you do?

Dear Family,

In class, I've been learning about expressing my opinions. I know that people have different opinions about things. It's important that I know how to tell my opinion in a way that is clear to other people.

Here are some ways you can help me practice expressing my opinions at home.

- Cut out pictures of food ads from the newspaper and put them in a pile. Then ask me to separate the pictures into foods I like and foods I don't like. When I'm done, let's talk about which foods you like and don't like.

- When we go to the grocery store, I can give my opinion about which items to buy such as cereal, soup, bread, snack foods, etc. We can also talk about how we don't always get what we want, like when I want to buy candy instead of vegetables!

- When we have family decisions to make, we can sit down and have everyone give his or her opinion. Then we can vote on what to do. For example, we might want to decide what our bedtime should be on weekends, where we should go on vacation, which movie we should watch, or what we should do on a rainy day.

We can have fun learning more about each other as we share our opinions!

Love,

____

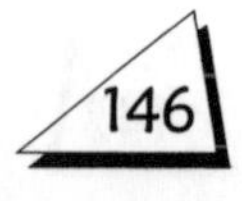

Inferencing: Overview

Inferencing is the ability to use one's prior knowledge and apply it to new information we see, hear, or read in order to deduce something. It is a skill we use daily, often without even being aware of it. Unfortunately, some students don't develop this skill on their own. As a result, they may experience difficulties in areas such as question comprehension, reading comprehension, identifying details, understanding important information, and justifying their opinions. The activities in this unit are designed to give your students an opportunity to practice this important language skill, helping them become better communicators.

Using the Activity Pages

- Before beginning the activities in this unit, talk about what it means to make inferences and why it's important.
- Review the vocabulary on each page. Teach any words that may be new to your students.
- As your students work through the activities, the inferences they make will become more complex. Talk about the connection between making inferences and making predictions.
- Send the activity pages home for additional practice.

Expansion Activities

- Help your students continue to practice making inferences. Take time during the week to discuss situations when your students have made inferences.
- Before beginning an activity, show your students the materials they'll be using. Ask your students to tell you what they think the activity is going to be and how they know.
- Before beginning a new story, ask your students to infer what the story is about based on the book's title or cover art only. As you read the story, stop periodically and ask your students to make inferences or predictions about why something happened or what will happen next based on what they know. Later, have students talk about whether their inferences were correct.

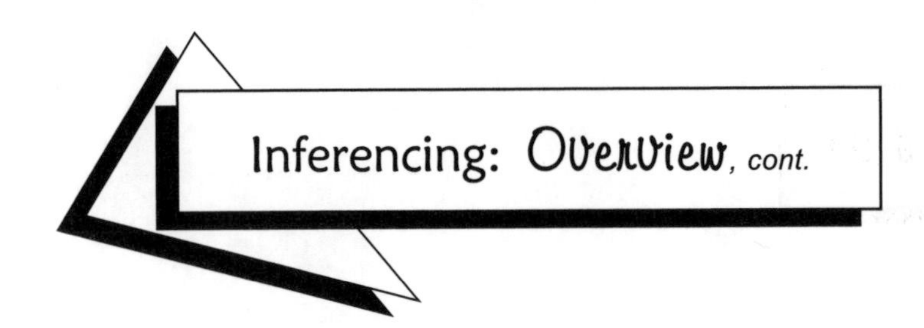

- As your students become more skilled at making inferences, talk about the fact that a person's inference about someone or something may or may not be correct. For example, if you saw a girl with a black eye, you might infer that the girl was in a fight. After talking to the girl, you find out that what actually happened is that she got hit by a softball during her game last night. Ask your students to tell about things they've inferred on a day-to-day basis and whether their inferences were right or wrong.

- Write brand names of items on index cards. Name the items one at a time and have your students tell what they think the product is and what it's used for.

- Have your students work with a partner to invent a product and give it a name. Then have each pair of students tell the name of their product and see if the other students can guess what it is.

- Make up new animals, like a "girelephant," and have your students draw pictures of what they think the animals would look like.

Name_______________________

	Days / Trials			Comments
Activity 1				
Activity 2				
Activity 3				
Activity 4				
Activity 5				
Activity 6				
Activity 7				
Activity 8				
Activity 9				
Activity 10				
Activity 11				
Activity 12				
Activity 13				
Activity 14				
Activity 15				
Activity 16				
Activity 17				
Activity 18				
Activity 19				
Activity 20				
Activity 21				
Activity 22				
Activity 23				
Activity 24				

Name______________________

Listen and then follow my directions.

1. It's supposed to rain today. Circle the picture that shows how you would know this.

2. This family has just finished eating dinner. Circle the picture that shows how you would know this.

3. Tami just finished washing her hair. Circle the picture that shows how you would know this.

Inferencing: Activity 2

Name________________________

Listen and then follow my directions.

1. Point to the picture that makes you think Byron is the one who spilled juice on the floor.

2. Point to the picture that makes you think these people are going on a trip.

3. Point to the picture that makes you think Gib's food is too hot.

Inferencing: Activity 3

Name___________________________

Listen and then follow my directions.

1. Mark an **X** on the picture that shows why you think it's morning. Tell why you think so.

2. Mark an **X** on the picture that shows why you might think the girl is going to school. Tell why you think so.

3. Mark an **X** on the picture that shows why you think it's autumn. Tell why you think so.

Inferencing: Activity 4

Name_______________________

Listen and then follow my directions.

1. Elizabeth was playing outside and lost her favorite necklace. Circle the picture that shows how you think Elizabeth felt. Tell why you think she felt that way.

2. Jerod and Bryant were having fun racing each other. Circle the picture that shows how you think they felt when they were finished. Tell why you think they felt that way.

3. Kristen found out she won first prize in a contest. Circle the picture that shows how you think Kristen felt. Tell why you think she felt that way.

4. Gary was going to the hospital to have his tonsils taken out. Circle the picture that shows how you think Gary felt. Tell why you think he felt that way.

Name________________________

Listen and then follow my directions.

1. Point to the picture that shows there is a fire. How do you know?

2. Point to the picture that shows there was a car accident. How do you know?

3. Point to the picture that shows someone is lost. How do you know?

Inferencing: *Activity* 6

Name________________________

Listen to what happened to each person. Then follow my directions.

1. Jeremy knew he wasn't supposed to play rough in the house. When his friend Kurt was over, they decided to play tag inside. While they were playing, Jeremy accidentally broke a lamp. Point to the picture that shows how Jeremy's mom felt. Tell why you think so.

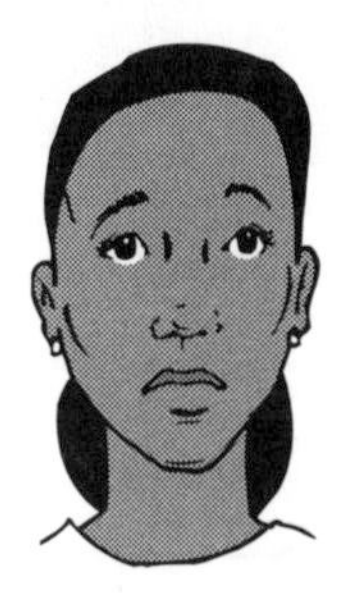  

2. Stacy found out her best friend was moving to California with her family. Point to the picture that shows how Stacy felt. Tell why you think so.

3. Emily was baby-sitting her brother Cody when a terrible thunderstorm began and the lights went out. Cody didn't like storms. Point to the picture that shows how Cody felt. Tell why you think so.

Inferencing: Activity 7

Name________________________

Look at the pictures and tell what kind of pet you think each child has. Then tell why you think that.

Inferencing: Activity 8

Name_______________________

Look at the pictures and tell what you think the people are going to do. Then tell why you think that.

Name________________________

Look at the pictures and tell what job you think each person does. Then tell why you think that.

Name_______________________

Look at the pictures and tell what sport you think each child likes to play. Then tell why you think that.

Inferencing: *Activity* 11

Name________________________

Look at the pictures and then answer my questions.

1. Why do you think Jessie's mom wants him to be quiet when he comes inside?

2. Why do you think Nicole is taking her shoes and socks off?

3. Why do you think Justis is crying?

4. Why do you think Morgan looks upset?

5. Why do you think the Jamisons bought so much food?

6. Why do you think the dog is barking?

Inferencing: *Activity* 12

Name______________________________

Listen and then draw a line to the picture that answers each question.

1. How do you know someone was cooking?

2. How do you know Donna is finished with her homework?

3. How do you know someone has been raking leaves?

4. How do you know the Masons are going to wash their car?

5. How do you know these people have a pet?

Inferencing: *Activity 13*

Name___________________________

Look at the pictures and then answer my questions.

1. What do you know about the music? How do you know?

2. What do you know about the food Mom is cooking? How do you know?

3. What is Mrs. Gray looking for? How do you know?

4. What is Mr. Miles going to do? How do you know?

Inferencing: Activity 14

Name________________________

Look at each picture and tell what you think will happen next. Tell why you think that.

Inferencing: Activity 15

Name________________________

Look at the pictures and then answer my questions.

1. What do you think the Campbells are going to do? Tell why you think so.

2. What kind of book do you think Angel is reading? Why do you think that?

3. What do you think happened? Tell why you think so.

4. What do you think happened? Why do you think that?

Inferencing: *Activity* 16

Name________________________

Look at the pictures and then answer my questions.

1. Michelle lost her mittens. What do you think her parents will say?

2. Philip wants to eat a cookie before dinner. What do you think his dad will say?

3. Crystal was excited when she found the markers she had lost. What do you think she'll do?

4. Cal forgot his homework. What do you think his teacher will do?

5. Daniel cleaned his room after school. What do you think his mom will say?

6. Taylor took her sister's CD without asking permission. What do you think Taylor's sister will say?

Inferencing: Activity 17

Name______________________

Look at the pictures and tell me what you know about each person.

1. What do you know about this man?

2. What do you know about this girl?

3. What do you know about the people who live here?

4. What do you know about the person who uses this room?

5. What do you know about the woman who is running into the building?

6. What do you know about the child who owns this bicycle?

Name________________________

Listen to each story I read and then tell where you think the people are.

1. The Kellers were sitting at a table talking. Soon the server brought their food. Everyone enjoyed their lunches.

    Where were the Kellers?

2. Isaac and his family were having a good time on vacation. They saw lots of animals. Isaac was really excited when he saw the big gorilla!

    Where were Isaac and his family?

3. Mr. Shield parked his car. He picked up the stack of letters on the seat and got out of the car. Then he went inside to buy some stamps and mail his letters.

    Where was Mr. Shield?

4. Dave was eager to get changed and join his friends. He could hear them laughing and splashing.

    Where do you think Dave's friends were?

5. While the Kemps were shopping, they went inside Darcie's favorite store. Darcie looked at the fish, birds, guinea pigs, and kittens. She liked them all.

    Where did Darcie like to go?

6. Greg and his friends were ready for a day full of fun and excitement! They bought their tickets and went inside. The very first thing they did was head for the giant roller coaster.

    Where were Greg and his friends?

Name____________________

Listen to each story and tell where you think the people are.

1. Mr. Stevens pushed the cart up and down each aisle. His cart was getting full. He had bread, cereal, fruits, vegetables, and meat. The only things left for Mr. Stevens to get were milk and eggs. Then he would be ready to check out.

   Where was Mr. Stevens? How do you know?

2. Chris and her grandparents walked into the big tent. There were three big rings on the floor. In the first ring, clowns were riding unicycles around in a circle. Chris thought they were funny. A lion tamer was working with lions in the second ring. They were jumping through hoops and doing other tricks. In the third ring, there were acrobats swinging on the flying trapeze. Chris couldn't believe how high in the air they were!

   Where were Chris and her grandparents?

3. Sam climbed to the top of the ladder. Then he sat down and *SWISH*, he was at the bottom. Sam stood up, ran around, and up the ladder he went again. Sam was having fun! Gina loved climbing on the monkey bars. She could almost make it to the top! Tony's favorite thing to do was swing. He tried to swing high enough to make his feet touch the branches of a tree. The children's mom enjoyed watching them play.

   Where were the children and their mom?

4. Sheila's class was on a field trip. The children were excited as they walked around. They saw lots of things on their field trip like dinosaur bones, mummies, and machines that showed how electricity works.

   Where was Sheila's class?

Name______________________

Listen and answer my questions.

1. Jessica said, "This spaghetti tastes like cardboard!" Do you think Jessica likes the spaghetti?

2. Dan said, "Having a dog is very expensive and it's too much work!" Do you think Dan wants a dog?

3. Mr. Jensen said, “Your report was very interesting, Yoshi.” Do you think Mr. Jensen liked Yoshi’s report?

4. When Sarah asked Patti to go shopping, Patti said, "Thanks, but I'd rather clean my room!" Do you think Patti likes to go shopping?

5. The Carters were stopped in traffic. Mr. Carter said, "I think we're going to be here a while!" Why do you think Mr. Carter said that?

6. The Kramers pulled into the parking lot. Mrs. Kramer said, "I don't think they're open." Why do you think Mrs. Kramer said that?

7. "Max, I'm so proud of you! You got all of your spelling words right!" Who do you think said that to Max?

8. "I don't think it's broken, but let's take an X-ray just to be sure." Who do you think said that?

9. "Come on guys! Let's get some hits this inning!" Who do you think said that?

10. "Tenesha, here's five dollars. Thank you for feeding our cat this weekend." Who do you think said that to Tenesha?

11. "Jacob, I want you to stay out of my room!" Who do you think said that to Jacob?

12. "Chloe, you may go, but I want you to come home before it gets dark outside." Who do think said that to Chloe?

Inferencing: Activity 21

Name________________________

1. What special day do you think it is? How do you know?
2. How old do you think Emily is today? How do you know?
3. How many people do you think she invited to her party? How do you know?
4. What do you think is in the round package?
5. What do you like to do on your birthday?

Inferencing: Activity 22

Name________________________

1. Where are the children?
2. What holiday is coming up? How do you know?
3. What subject are the children learning right now? How do you know?
4. Which student knows the answer? How do you know?
5. What else do the children do at school? How do you know?
6. Do you go to school? What do you like best about school?

Inferencing: *Activity 23*

Name______________________

1. What do you think the weather is like? Why?
2. Do you think the people that live here are home? Why?
3. Where do you think the people who live here might be?
4. Do you think the man ringing the doorbell lives here? Why?
5. Where would you like to go on vacation? Why do you want to go there?

Inferencing: Activity 24

Name________________________

1. What season is it? How do you know?
2. Where are the people? How do you know?
3. What do you think happened to the person with the broken leg? What makes you think that?
4. Do you think all of the people go skiing? What else could they do?
5. Have you ever been snow skiing? What was it like? If you haven't skied, would you like to try it?

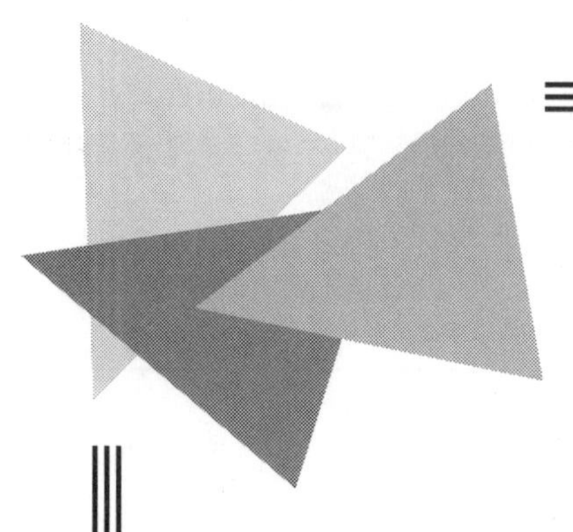

Dear Family,

I've been learning to make inferences. I know that first I have to think about what I already know. Then I have to figure out what else I know from what I see, hear, or read. You can help me at home by doing some of the activities below with me.

- Show me photographs or pictures from magazines of different places. Ask me to look at each picture and tell where it is.
- When we go shopping, show me new things and ask me if I can figure out what each item is or what it's used for.
- When we're watching TV or a movie, turn off the sound and ask me to tell you what I think the people are saying or doing.
- Point out things we see and ask me to tell you what I know. For example, if we drive by a school parking lot on a weekday and it's empty, I could tell you that there's no school. Or when the neighbor's car is in his driveway on a weekday, I might tell you I think he's sick because he's not at work.
- Ask me about everyday things and how I know certain information. You might ask me to tell you how I know certain things like when it's time for dinner before you tell me, when it's not a good time to ask a question (like when you're on the phone), or when it's time to mow the lawn.
- Read books with me. While we're reading, ask me questions about where the characters are or what I think will happen next.

I love learning new things with you. Thanks for helping me!

Love,

____

Answer Key

▸▸▸Reasoning

page 10
Point to:
1. blanket
2. rake
3. rain

page 11
Circle:
1. burnt toast
2. apple
3. rabbits eating plants

page 12
Circle:
1. dish towel
2. CD player
3. boards

page 13
Mark an **X** on:
1. dead plants/dry stream
2. crayons/paper
3. bat/baseball

page 14
1. The woman is sweeping up a mess. Circle the boy dropping a tray.
2. The boy is putting on his mittens. Circle the children sledding.
3. The woman is doing laundry. Circle the boys playing in the mud.

page 15
1. The boy feels sick. Circle the boy eating junk food.
2. The woman is cleaning the floor. Circle the dirty floor.
3. A man is getting his glasses. Circle the man reading.

page 16
1. The people are watering their flowers. Mark an **X** on the rain.
2. The girl is washing her bicycle. Mark an **X** on the girl riding on the dry sidewalk.
3. The man is dressed up. Mark an **X** on the man raking leaves.

page 17
Mark an **X** on:
1. the burglar robbing a house; the car accident
2. the girl riding her bicycle; the girl in-line skating

page 18
Mark an **X** on:
1. hoe
2. vacuum cleaner
3. TV

page 19
1. Yes
2. No
3. Yes
4. Yes
5. No
6. No
7. Yes
8. No
9. Yes
10. No
11. Yes
12. Yes
13. Yes
14. Yes

page 20
1. Yes
2. Yes
3. No
4. Yes
5. No
6. No
7. Yes
8. Yes
9. No
10. Yes
11. Yes
12. No
13. Yes
14. Yes

page 21
1. Yes
2. Yes
3. No
4. Yes
5. Yes
6. Yes
7. No
8. Yes
9. Yes
10. Yes
11. No
12. No
13. Yes
14. No

page 22
1. Some
2. All
3. Some
4. All
5. Some
6. Some
7. All
8. Some
9. All
10. Some
11. Some
12. Some
13. All
14. All

page 23
1. No
2. No
3. Yes
4. Yes
5. No
6. Yes
7. Yes
8. Yes
9. Yes
10. No
11. No
12. Yes
13. No
14. No

page 24
1. to keep it cold
2. to eat
3. to keep in touch with friends/ family members
4. because it gets too long
5. to earn money to buy things they need and want
6. because they're funny
7. to stay healthy
8. so they'll run

page 25
1. to get someplace we want to go
2. to stay dry when it's raining
3. to keep our hands warm
4. to stay healthy
5. to protect our feet
6. to stay clean
7. to keep them clean
8. to play
9. to get our hands and bodies clean
10. to keep them warm
11. because they like animals
12. to stay healthy, because they like them
13. for fun, to learn
14. to stay safe, to keep people out
15. to erase something when they make a mistake or want to write something else

page 26
1. It ruins the walls.
2. It hurts people.
3. We might slip and fall.
4. We might start a fire.
5. The dog may not be friendly.
6. A stranger might hurt us.
7. It will ruin the book.
8. We might get burned.

9. We might fall in and drown.
10. We might fall off and get hurt.

page 27

1. a
2. b
3. b

page 28

1. bed
2. puppies
3. TV
4. eat
5. zoo
6. swims
7. hands
8. pencil

page 29

1. cold
2. soft
3. sad, scared
4. hot
5. slow
6. dark
7. down
8. round
9. small
10. the water
11. meows
12. washing machine
13. football, soccer ball
14. green
15. glass

page 30

1. to play on the playground equipment
2. The chain is broken.
3. It looks like it's going to storm (clouds, windy, etc.).
4. Answers will vary.
5. Answers will vary.

page 31

1. No, because they might bite or attack you.
2. some
3. Point to the bucket and the long-handled brush.
4. He hasn't eaten his food.
5. a veterinarian
6. so they don't get loose and run away or hurt the people visiting the zoo

page 32

1. Mark an **X** on the chalkboard and the easel.
2. the blocks
3. some
4. the number rug
5. markers or crayons
6. Answers will vary.

page 33

1. yes
2. the ice cream
3. to clean up the box of cereal that spilled on the floor
4. grocery carts or shopping baskets
5. paper or plastic bags
6. gas station

▸▸▸Sequencing

page 38

Circle:

1. Nate pouring milk on cereal
2. Bailey opening the present
3. Mrs. Carney mowing the grass

page 39

Point to:

1. dog with long hair
2. dirty shirt
3. clown with no make-up
4. paper with no picture

page 40

Mark an **X** on:

1. folded laundry
2. boy standing next to the finished snowman
3. boy walking to school
4. clean room

page 41

Point to:

1. boy getting a drink
2. shaded car
3. Kayla frosting the cake
4. Jeremy getting a glass out of the cupboard

page 42

Circle:

1. the fourth chair
2. woman walking out the door
3. Mrs. Cunnick locking her door
4. Tyler turning off the light

page 43

1. 
2. 
3. 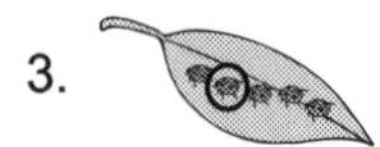

page 44

1.   
2.   
3. 

page 45

1. 12
2. A
3. ☺☺☺☹
4. □□▫□

page 46

1.  
2. 
3. 

page 47

1. 2 1 3
   Carrie wanted to take her dog for a walk. First, she got the leash. Next, she put the leash on her dog. Last, she took her dog outside and went for a walk.
2. 3 2 1
   First, Bobby wrote a letter to his aunt. Next, he put the letter in the envelope. Then he put a stamp on the letter and mailed it.

page 48

1. 3 2 1
   First, Kevin put toothpaste on his toothbrush. Next, he brushed his teeth. Last, he rinsed off his toothbrush.
2. 3 2 1
   First, the bird found a place to build her nest and started with a few pieces of grass. Then the bird made the nest bigger. Last, the bird sat in her finished nest.

page 49

1. 3 1 2
   First, Barry got out some paper and crayons. Next, he colored a picture. Last, he gave the picture to his dad and his dad hung it on the refrigerator.
2. 3 2 1
   First, Stephanie took some food out of the refrigerator. Next, she made a sandwich. Last, she ate the sandwich for lunch.

page 50

First, the girl went to the salon to get her hair cut. Next, the stylist put the cape on the girl. Then the stylist cut the girl's hair. Last, the girl paid for her haircut and left the salon.

page 51

First, the woman got a flower and went to the backyard. Then she dug a small hole. Next, she planted the flower in the hole. Last, she watered the plant.

page 52

The children wanted to build a snowman. First, they put on their winter clothes and went outside. Next, they rolled a big snowball. Then they rolled two smaller snowballs. The children put the two small snowballs on top of the big one. Then they gave the snowman two eyes, a nose, and some buttons. Last, (answers will vary).

page 53

The Millers were going on a camping trip. First, they packed their suitcases and got their other supplies ready. Next, they loaded everything in the car. Then they drove to the campsite. When they got there, they put up their tent and gathered wood for a fire. Then they went fishing. Last, (answers will vary).

page 54

Students retell the stories in the correct order.

page 55

Students follow directions as they are given.

page 56

Answers may vary. Suggestions are given.

1. First, I take out the dog food. Then I pour some in my dog's bowl. Last, I put the dog food away.
2. First, I dig a small hole. Then I put the flower in the hole and put dirt around it. Last, I water the flower.
3. First, I peel the banana. Then I eat it. Last, I throw the peel away.
4. First, I get out a sheet of paper and some crayons. Then I color a picture. Last, I put the crayons away.
5. First, I turn on the TV. Then I change the channel to cartoons. Last, I turn off the TV.
6. First, I get a tissue. Next, I blow my nose. Then I throw the tissue in the trash. Last, I wash my hands.
7. First, I take out my toothbrush and toothpaste. Next, I run my toothbrush under the water and put toothpaste on it. Then I brush my teeth. Last, I put toothbrush and toothpaste away.

8. First, I take off my clothes and put on my pajamas. Then I brush my teeth. Last, I get into bed and turn off the light.
9. First, I take a slice of bread out of the package. Then I put the bread in the toaster and push down the lever. Last, I put butter on my toast.
10. First, we decide who is "it." Then we all try to run away from the person who is "it" so we don't get tagged. When someone gets tagged, then he is "it."
11. First, I look up the number in the phone book. Next, I dial the phone. When the person answers, I say "hello." When we're finished talking, I say "good-bye" and hang up.
12. First, we get a deck of cards. Then one person deals each player seven cards. Next, we each take turns asking another player for a card. Finally, when one player doesn't have any cards left, the game is over.
13. First, I gather the dirty clothes. Then I sort them into piles. Next, I put one pile in the washing machine and add the soap. When the clothes are washed, I put them in the drier. Finally, I fold the dry clothes and put them away.
14. First, I take a big breath. Then I blow air into the balloon. I do this several times until the balloon is big. Finally, I tie the end of the balloon.
15. First, I sit down and look at the menu. Then I tell the server what I want to order. When my food comes, I eat it. Last, I pay the check and leave a tip for the server.
16. First, I take out my keys. Then I put the key in the keyhole and turn it. Next, I open the door and walk inside. Last, I shut the door and lock it again.
17. First, I get my bat and glove and go to the ballpark. When it is my turn, I try to hit the ball. Then I run around the bases. When my team has three outs, I go to the outfield. Last, I go back home.
18. First, I turn on the TV and decide which game to play. Then I hit START. Next, I play the game until I am finished. Last, I turn off the TV.
19. First, I take the pillow off the bed. Then I pull up the sheet and blanket. Next, I straighten out the comforter. Last, I put the pillow back on the bed.
20. First, I put the crust on the pizza pan. Then I spread sauce on the crust. Next, I add my ingredients and put the pizza in the oven. When the pizza is finished baking, I cut it and eat it. Last, I clean up my mess.

page 57
Answers will vary.

page 58
1. bought their tickets
2. bought some popcorn and sodas
3. Answers will vary.
4. Answers will vary.
5. Answers will vary.

page 59
1. Point to the boy racing through the cones.
2. Point to the child in the left lane. Then point to the child in the middle lane.
3. the first one
4. no, the third child
5. Answers will vary, but all should use sequence words.
6. Answers will vary.

page 60
1. help with the chores on the farm
2. fed the chickens
3. sweep out the barn
4. First, they helped their uncle catch the horses. Then they saddled the horses and went horseback riding.
5. Answers will vary.
6. Answers will vary.

page 61
1. take a shower
2. getting an inner tube
3. put the inner tube in the water and get in
4. jump or dive off of the diving board
5. get out of the pool, dry off, and then get dressed
6. Answers will vary.

▶▶▶Cause & Effect

page 66
1. It's torn. Circle Jason catching his shirt on the fence post.
2. It's broken. Circle the boys playing catch.

page 67
1. She skinned it. Circle the girl in-line skating.
2. It's flat. Circle the boy riding over glass/trash.

page 68
1. It's torn. Mark an **X** on the girl carrying the book by one of its pages.
2. They're laughing. Mark an **X** on the children watching TV.

page 69
1. It's melting. Circle the sunny day.
2. He's wet. Circle the man walking in the rain.

page 70
Point to:
1. the rainy day
2. the boys playing football

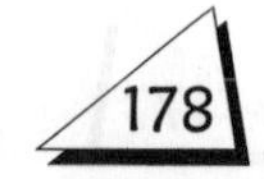

page 71
Mark an **X** on:
1. Nathan coloring on the wall
2. Mrs. Meyers trying to open a jar
3. Caitlin having a snack before dinner

page 72
Mark an **X** on:
1. kite stuck in the tree
2. growling dog
3. girl sitting in a dentist chair

page 73
Mark an **X** on:
1. melted ice cream
2. cat climbing the tree
3. horse jumping over the fence
4. man handing the boy some money

page 74
Circle:
1. legs with scratches on them
2. Lisa stubbing her toe on the sidewalk
3. dead/wilted plants
4. flooded building

page 75
Mark an **X** on:
1. farmer locking gate
2. spelling words with +10
3. Denise smiling and holding the cat
4. puppy sleeping in his bed

page 76

page 77

page 78

page 79
Answers will vary. Suggestions are given.
1. Someone might fall.
2. You might get stuck.
3. You might get cavities.
4. You won't be able to unlock your door.
5. Someone might steal it.
6. Your might get a bad grade.
7. You might get lost.
8. You might get a stomachache.

page 80
Answers will vary. Suggestions are given.
1. It dried out.
2. It was raining.
3. She fell off the swings.
4. The wind blew it up there.
5. Someone drove through it.
6. It rained.
7. Someone told a joke.
8. The wind blew it.

page 81
Answers will vary. Suggestions are given.
1. It would make him happy.
2. He'll be hungry.
3. Your friend will share lunch with you.
4. You'll go after your mom gets home.
5. Your dad will worry about your brother, and he will be upset that you forgot to give him the message.
6. You'll plan to do something inside.
7. Your handwriting won't be as neat.
8. It would make her have a nice day.

page 82
Answers will vary. Suggestions are given.
1. It will freeze.
2. A car might run over it.
3. You might trip on your shoelaces.
4. You might not get better as quickly.
5. It might break.
6. It might run out of gas and stop.
7. You'll stink.
8. She might get hurt in an accident.
9. He might start a fire.
10. You might cut your foot.
11. The dog might run away.
12. It might burn.
13. You will get cold.
14. You might oversleep and be late.
15. Your mom might worry and you'll get in trouble.

page 83
Answers will vary. Suggestions are given.
1. There might be a car accident or a fire.
2. It might be glad to see you.
3. It might be raining or too cold outside.
4. He might have acted meanly toward another child.

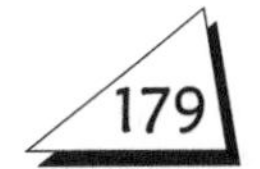

5. She might be tired or hungry or have a dirty diaper.
6. He might have stayed up too late the night before.
7. It might be her birthday.
8. Her horse might have won first place.
9. He might have broken his arm or leg.
10. The electricity may be out or the light bulb might be burned out.
11. The dog might have run away.
12. Chris might have forgotten to bring it home.
13. Someone might have tipped it over.
14. It might have run out of gas or gotten a flat tire.
15. She might be allergic to something.

page 84

1. They went to the store to buy Jessie's grandmother a birthday card.
2. He was sad. He lost his favorite book.
3. She ran home. A barking dog scared her.
4. No. Carter was sick.
5. Beth wore special ear muffs. The noise would hurt their ears.

page 85

1. He blew his whistle and yelled, "Walk!" Someone was running.
2. The librarian asked them to leave. They were talking too loudly.
3. He ran to the door. His grandparents had arrived.
4. They went sledding. There was so much snow that school was canceled.
5. It's for the Save the Whales Organization. They might die.

page 86

Answers will vary for the reason each thing would have or would not have made Valerie happy.

Circle:
Valerie running with puppy
Valerie hugging Grandma
Valerie blowing out birthday candles
Valerie running through sprinkler

Cross out:
Valerie falling
Valerie with broken arm
Valerie sick in bed

page 87

1. so Abby doesn't get burned when Mrs. Malone opens the oven
2. potholders/hot pads
   She might burn her hands.
3. The water is starting to boil.
   The water will boil over.
4. There may not be enough food for everyone.
5. Answers will vary.

page 88

1. He fell. He tripped over the branch.
2. He won the race.
3. They might go too fast or fall off.
4. They might get hurt.
5. Answers will vary.

page 89

1. He left his bike out in the rain.
2. The rain would water her vegetable garden in the backyard and her flowers near the front porch.
3. The newspaper was getting wet.
4. playing in the puddles
   yes, because they're smiling and having fun
5. Answers will vary.

▸▸▸Problem Solving

page 94

Circle:
1. towel, soap
2. tape, wrapping paper
3. Carrie at the doctor's office, Carrie in bed resting

page 95

Circle:
1. camera, film
2. bread, peanut butter, knife
3. stationery, stamp, pen, envelope

page 96

1. mixing bowl, eggs, oil, water, pan
2. toothpaste
3. baseball, glove
4. teacups

page 97

Mark an **X** on:
1. Kimberly mopping up the spill
2. Jason standing on a stepstool
3. Kayla shutting the curtains

page 98

Circle:
1. tape
2. Jacob playing
3. Courtney picking up her brother

page 99

Mark an **X** on:
1. Dylan asking his mom for help
2. Teresa sharpening her pencil
3. the children sharing the apple

page 100

1. Anita's bicycle tire is flat.
2. Mr. Philips left the door to his birdcage open.
3. Ling spilled something on her friend's shirt.
4. Keesha's brother is making so much noise that she can't hear her friend on the phone.

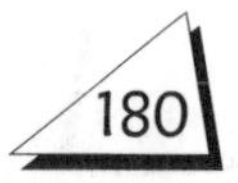

page 101
Circle:
1. Elena talking to the lifeguard
2. Ben talking to his mom
3. Kenesha talking to a teacher

page 102
Answers will vary. Suggestions are given.
1. Noah forgot his swimsuit. He should tell his teacher and his parent.
2. Mariah doesn't have any crayons. She could use markers or colored pencils.
3. Drew can't tie his shoes. He could wear different shoes.
4. The zipper on Amanda's coat is stuck. She should ask a grown-up for help.

page 103

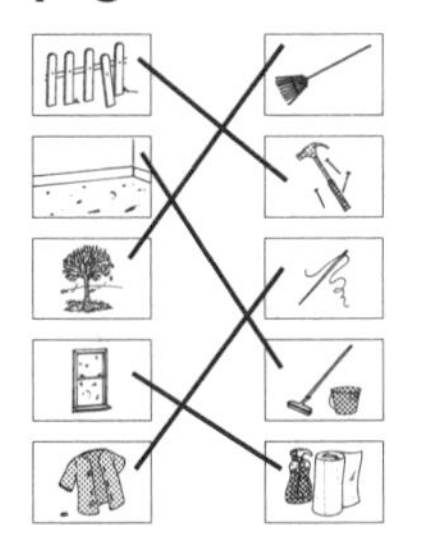

page 104
1. Circle the microscope.
2. Mark an **X** on the ruler.
3. Draw a line under the scissors.
4. Draw a line through the flashlight.
5. Draw a box around the water bottle.

page 105
Answers will vary for what the child would do to solve the problem.
1. The doll's arm is broken off.
2. There's a spider on the wall.
3. The boy missed his bus.
4. The boy has gum all over his face.

page 106
Answers will vary for what the child would do to solve the problem.
1. The milk carton is leaking.
2. The mug is cracked.
3. The girl is swinging her yo-yo too close to the boy.
4. The boy's shoelaces have knots in them.
5. The girl is standing on a rocking chair and it's tipping.
6. The vacuum cleaner cord is tipping over a plant.

page 107
1. The boy is coloring on the wall. Martha should have put the crayons away when she was done coloring her picture.
2. The dog is going to eat the sandwich. The person could have put his sandwich in the middle of the table until he sat down.
3. It's raining in the window. Someone should have shut the window when it started raining.
4. The woman is tripping on a skateboard left on the sidewalk. The children could have put the skateboard away when they were done playing with it.

page 108
Answers will vary for the second half of each question.
1. It's raining and Trent doesn't have a raincoat so he decides not to go to his friend's house.
2. Daniel and Troy can't find any cardboard boxes to use to build a clubhouse.
3. Katie doesn't have any money to buy her mom a birthday present.
4. Mitzi can't get her locker open to get her science book.

page 109
Answers will vary for the third part of each question.
1. Josh left his glasses at his friend's house. Josh called his friend and asked him to bring the glasses to school the next day.
2. Maria's friend Amy is moving. Maria and Amy decide to write letters to keep in touch.
3. Sheila got invited to a slumber party, but she's never spent the night away from home before. Sheila decided not to go to the party.

page 110
Answers will vary. Suggestions are given.
1. Kyle could borrow the book from a friend or get it from the library.
2. Mr. Miles could get the medicine himself or ask someone else to get it for him.
3. Claudia could go to the store to get some soup or eat something else for lunch.
4. Mr. Dexter could ride with someone to work or have someone bring his work home.

page 111
Answers will vary. Suggestions are given.
1. pharmacy, grocery store
2. grocery store, convenience store
3. shopping mall
4. hardware store
5. dentist
6. grocery store
7. veterinarian
8. optometrist

page 112
Answers will vary. Suggestions are given.
1. go to the nurse's office

2. look in the phone book
3. look at a calendar
4. give it back to the person it belongs to
5. tell your parent, call the bus garage
6. try to catch the dog and bring it back to your neighbor
7. ask your teacher to repeat it
8. tell an adult or get a towel and clean it up
9. go to a neighbor's home and wait for someone from your family to get home
10. get a flashlight or light a candle
11. yell out the window
12. listen to your sister
13. wait until he's finished talking on the phone
14. run to a phone and call 911
15. stay quietly in your home without opening the door

page 113
Answers will vary. Suggestions are given.
1. tell your teacher
2. read the game instructions
3. try to call her again later
4. look up its meaning in the dictionary
5. look for the leash until you find it
6. try to convince the person to give the money back
7. call your family members so they don't worry
8. apologize and ask her for another one
9. call 911
10. quickly run outside
11. say "No!"
12. confess and then apologize to your friend
13. talk to her and listen to her, invite her over to play
14. tell an adult, ask the person if she is okay
15. tell an adult, talk to your friend

page 114
Answers will vary. Suggestions are given.
1. move in front of the taller people or sit on her dad's shoulders
2. The parade is stopped. He could get people to help him push the car and the float to the side of the road.
3. It's going to hit the stoplight. They should pull the balloon around the stoplight.
4. It might rain. All the floats and the people will get wet. The people watching the parade should get ready to leave. The people in charge of the parade should let the parade continue as planned.
5. Answers will vary.

page 115
1. They don't want people to get food or drinks on the exhibits.
2. They don't want people to damage the skeleton. The person might get asked to leave the museum.
3. so people don't touch it
4. roping off areas
5. Answers will vary.
   so children can learn by touching and doing
6. Answers will vary.

page 116
1. He didn't have enough money to golf. He could ask Wes to borrow $1.00. He could have called to find out how much it cost to golf.
2. Answers will vary.
3. in the windmill
   Answers will vary.
4. Answers will vary.
5. Answers will vary.

page 117
1. It's cold, snowy, and icy. People could slip and fall on the ice.
2. They put up a sign in the parking lot.
3. Problems: A child is walking by herself, the woman carrying the bag can't see over it, and the shopping cart is rolling toward the car.
   Solutions: Answers will vary.
4. Answers will vary.
5. Answers will vary.

▸▸▸Opinions

Answers will vary for all items in this unit.

▸▸▸Inferencing

page 150
Circle:
1. man carrying the umbrella
2. people washing and putting away dishes
3. Tami with her hair wrapped in a towel

page 151
Point to:
1. boy drinking/dribbling
2. people at the airport
3. Gib with his mouth open, steam coming off of his food

page 152
Mark an **X** on:
1. boy sitting at a table with cereal and milk
2. girl wearing a backpack and walking toward a school bus
3. trees with leaves on the ground